PINTO!

PINTO!

Based Upon the
True Story of the
Longest Horseback
Ride in History

M.J. Evans

DANCING HORSE PRESS / FOXFIELD,
COLORADO

M.J. Evans/Dancing Horse Press
7013 S. Telluride St.
Foxfield, CO 80016

www.dancinghorsepress.com

Publisher's Cataloging-In-Publication Data
Names: Evans, M.J., author.
Title: Pinto! : Based Upon the True Story of the
    Longest Horseback Ride in History / M.J.
    Evans.
Description: Foxfield, Colorado : Dancing Horse
    Press, [2019] | Interest age level: 9 and up.
    | Includes bibliographical references. |
    Summary: "Pinto! is based upon the true story
    of four horsemen who seek fame and fortune by
    embarking on a three-year, twenty-thousand-
    mile journey around the United States. Only
    one horse completed the entire trip and lived
    to tell about it"-- Provided by publisher.
Identifiers: ISBN 9781733020411 (print) | ISBN
    9781733020428 (ebook)
Subjects: LCSH: Horses--United States--History--
    20th century--Juvenile fiction. | Horsemen and
    horsewomen--Travel--United States--History--
    20th century--Juvenile fiction. | United
    States--History--1901-1953--Juvenile fiction.
    | CYAC: Horses--United States--History--20th
    century--Fiction. | Horsemen and horsewomen--
    Travel--United States--History--20th century--
    Fiction. | United States--History--1901-1953--
    Fiction. | LCGFT: Historical fiction.
Classification: LCC PZ7.E8917 Pi 2019 (print) |
    LCC PZ7.E8917 (ebook) | DDC [Fic]--dc23

Ordering Information: Special discounts are available on quantity purchases by corporations, associations, and others. For details, contact the publisher at the address above.   Printed in the United States of America

For everyone who had a dream , reached for it and held on. Maybe no one else cared, but you did, and there is a treasure to be had in knowing that.

Contents

"We're born to the saddle. We have the nags and gear. Let's ride to every state Capital in the Union. Let's get ourselves a reputation. Let's make the longest horseback ride on record!" George W. Beck

PINTO!

I am a little horse with big dreams. I was living on Bainbridge Island in Puget Sound in the state of Washington. If I had stayed there, those dreams would never have come true. But then came the day I was purchased by George Beck, a man who also had big dreams. That was in the year 1912. Together, with three other men on horseback, and a flea-bitten dog named Nip, we completed a twenty thousand-mile journey over the span of three years. Of the seventeen horses who joined us for a time on the trip, only one horse made it the whole way—me!

CHAPTER 1

Meeting George Beck

Spring was coming. That is to say, the rain was getting warmer. Such was the only thing I was happy about. I was living in a poorly fenced paddock set far back from the road and partly concealed behind several of the thousands of giant Douglas Fir trees that covered the Pacific Northwest where I was born. The mud-soaked corral, in which I spent most of my time of late, was causing the frogs in the soles of my hooves to itch with thrush.

I hadn't been in this paddock on Bainbridge Island with the five other horses for many days. The man who owned all the horses was not attached to us, nor we to him. He was a horse trader. His only intent was selling us and making a quick profit. Oh, he was kind enough, as kind as that type of man is. Not a horseman, you see. Just a businessman. Buy a horse, sell it quickly, not caring what kind of home the horse went to. But, as I say, he was a decent man, as men go, always giving us plenty of fresh hay and an occasional scoop of oats.

The other horses in the paddock with me were much older than I was. They spent each day sharing stories about their lives and how they came to be in this place. I hadn't done much of anything yet, so I just listened. Oh, I had my dreams, as every young horse does, but I kept those to myself for fear they would think me silly and laugh at me.

One old, swaybacked mare, who enjoyed standing beside me, told me about the day she was in a parade. "It was the proudest moment of my life," she said. "The little boy who owned me dressed me up with ribbons and leg wraps. My saddle and bridle were polished until they shone nearly as much as I did. We pranced down the streets of the town as music played from a brass band. People cheered as we went by. It was all so very grand."

"I have had a very hard life," said a large, black gelding. "I have spent most of my life hitched to a thick harness pulling logs out of the forest."

I glanced down at his shoulders and noticed the scars left there from years of throwing all his strength, against a thick, leather collar. I felt sorry for him and hoped that was not in my future.

One small pony sidled up to me. "I have spent my whole life teaching children how to ride. I was kind and patient with all of them. Never once did I buck any of them off."

"Then why are you here?" I asked.

"The children grew up and went away. Now, I can only hope that another nice family with little children takes me home with them."

All these stories made me wonder what was in store for me. I realized I'm not an ordinary quarter horse or draft horse. I am a Morab. That means I am half Morgan and half Arabian. I have seen my reflection in the spring-fed water trough, and I am quite aware of how spectacular I am. I'm not tall, only fifteen hands, but sturdy as a boulder and well proportioned. I have a thick, elegantly arched neck. My croup—the top of my hips—is well-rounded, and my hindquarters are well-muscled. But my most outstanding feature is my coloring. I am a beautiful black and white pinto with large patches of both colors all over my body. And the dream I held in my heart was that someday I would accomplish something great, maybe even become famous.

"You'll be the first to go, mark my words," the swaybacked mare said to me the second day we were together. "Unless some little children come to get the pony."

I knew she was right. Between my beauty and my youth, I was sure someone would want to take me home with them.

I remember distinctly the day I met the man named George Beck who was to become my master. That was the day my life changed forever. I was standing in the muddy paddock with the other horses, listening to their stories. Our heads were bowed to let the rain drip off our forelocks, protecting our eyes. My ears pricked forward when I heard the men's voices as they approached. One voice I recognized as belonging to my owner. His voice was high-pitched and always a bit too loud, whether he was talking to us or to people who came to look us over. The other voice I did not recognize.

I lifted my head and watched the two men as they came up to the fence. Resting their arms on the rail, they peered at the group of wet, shivering, muddy, and quite bored horses, of which I was one. I looked at the new man. He was tall and thin. His face was clean-shaven, and a shock of curly, brown hair stuck out from under the brim of his hat. But what attracted me to him was something about his face and eyes. I sensed immediately that he was a horseman. I could tell, just by looking at him, that this gentleman had a quick eye for horses. A surge of hope passed through me. Perhaps this was the man who would take me away and help me do something truly great, something deserving of my heritage.

I pawed the mud and splashed the puddle in front of me. I nickered and trotted around in a circle, sure that he would notice me, even in my wet and muddy condition. To be sure that I wouldn't be missed, I sloshed across the paddock, right up to him, and put my nose in his face.

Both men laughed.

"I guess he likes you," our owner said.

"Seems so. What is he?" the new gentleman asked as he stroked the wide, white blaze covering most of my face.

"He's called a Morab, half Arab, half Morgan. A sturdier, more dependable beast you'll not find anywhere on the island or the mainland."

"Well, that's sure what I need for this journey," the man said as he opened the gate and entered our paddock. His large boots made sucking sounds in the mud as he walked up to me. I stood perfectly still when he examined my eyes and put his fingers in my mouth so he could look at my teeth. He ran his large, rough but gentle hands down my legs, over my barrel, and across my spine.

Seeming to be pleased, he stepped back and smiled. "He's not very big but he appears to be strong and healthy enough. What's his name?"

"Never gave him one."

"Then I'll call him 'Pinto.'"

And that's how George Beck chose me to join him on his twenty thousand-mile journey.

CHAPTER 2

Preparing for a Historic Trip

The next day, George Beck rode up to the paddock on a strong bay gelding. He dismounted and entered the paddock with a halter and lead in his hand. "Come with me, Pinto," he said. "We're going on a great adventure together."

I liked the sound of that.

He placed the halter over my head and gave me a pat on my arched neck.

I followed him out the gate, glancing back at the other horses to bid farewell. The old mare whinnied after me. The pony dropped his cute, little head.

My new master mounted the gelding, who I learned was named Lad, and led me through the village to the shore where we got on a ferry. The rolling movement of the boat across the water of Elliot Bay was a bit frightening but since Lad seemed at ease, I decided all was well and stood quietly next to him. My ears twitched, picking up the sound of the splashing water as the ferry broke through the surface. My nostrils flared at the scent of saltwater and fish.

The ferry docked with a jolt at a village named "Brownsville," and we continued our journey down dirt logging roads until we reached the village of Shelton. We turned off the road when we came upon a small house with a barn set off to the side. A neat, wooden fence formed a paddock around the barn. It was here that George dismounted.

Though I was a young horse, just six years of age, I had been well trained to carry a saddle and rider and hold a bit gently in my mouth. I soon learned, however, that George Beck had not purchased me as a riding horse.

"How do you like Pinto?" George said as we entered the barnyard and approached three men. "He's going to be our pack horse."

A pack horse? He wanted me for a pack horse? That was not at all what I had in mind and I wasn't sure I liked this idea. I am far too beautiful to have my black and white patches covered up with oil-skin bags and ropes. How would I ever do great things and become famous for being a pack horse?

"Do you think he's big enough? Strong enough?" one of the men said.

"I know horses, Charles," George said. "I know how to pick 'em. This little fella may be short but he's sturdy. Besides, I like the look in his eye."

I blinked.

Over the next few days, George and Charles, who I later learned was George's brother, came to the paddock carrying bundles of bags and ropes.

"I brought some oil skin bags to put the grain in," George said.

"I have some bedrolls and a few tin plates and cups," Charles said, dropping his load on the ground with a huff. The bundle clanged and rattled as it hit the ground.

The two other men that I met on the first day were named Jay and Ray. They called Ray "Fat," though I couldn't understand why as he was as tall and skinny as the fir trees that surrounded us. They brought supplies as well. I stood patiently as the four men burdened me down with bags, first one way, then another. When everything was on my back, I was carrying nearly two hundred pounds. It was a good thing I was strong.

"I think we should put the feed bags on the top," Fat said as he untied the ropes and took off some bags. "Seems like they could wobble and cause Pinto to lose his balance if they hang down too low."

"How about if we put our bedrolls on the back of each of our saddles," Jay suggested. "That will take some of the weight off Pinto."

"The coffee pot and plates make too much noise if we put them in a bag by themselves," Charles said. "Let's wrap them up in some of our extra clothes."

The fiddling and rearranging went on for several days. It didn't bother me any, as long as there was a cool drink of water and a bucket of oats at the end, which George Beck always made sure to provide. Besides, I had already grown to like George and I was eager to show him how strong and dependable I was.

There were four other horses living with me in the small barn in the village of Shelton, Washington. Their names were Lad, who brought my master to fetch me, Bill, Dick, and Blaze. I never thought Blaze had a blaze as fine as mine, but I guess he had the name first. I soon learned that the four of them were to be the riding horses. They were all nice enough, though Bill seemed to be getting a bit old and often complained to me that his hocks were sore. But since he appeared to walk and trot just fine, the men had no idea he was uncomfortable. I admired Bill's determination and great work ethic.

Whenever the men were with us, they talked about the long journey we were soon to embark upon.

"There's gold at the end of the rainbow and the rainbow is landing in San Francisco on June first three years from now. We're going to be there to collect it," George Beck said, over and over.

"The World's Fair, the Panama-Pacific International Exposition, is going to be a huge event," Charles Beck said, who the men started calling 'Slim.' Fiddling with the knots on the pack, he continued: "People from all over the world will be there to celebrate the completion of the Panama Canal. It is going to open on February 20, 1915, and run until almost Christmas."

"Did you hear that the Liberty Bell will be transported cross-country by railroad to be on display?" George said. "And the world's first steam locomotive will be there, too, among many marvels of the new century. There will even be a telephone line from New York to the West Coast. But they're all in for a big surprise. The best exhibit will be four horsemen called the 'Overland Westerners.' Everyone will want to meet us."

"Just think," Fat said, "we are going to visit every state capital in the Union. No one has ever done that before."

"We are going to complete the longest, overland horseback ride in history," George added. "We'll see things no one else has ever seen, and do things no one else has ever done."

"We're going to be famous," Jay said as he tucked oats into a canvas bag. "There'll be books written about us. Maybe even a movie."

I learned that movies were a new thing, described as "moving pictures," that people watched in darkened rooms in big buildings. George talked a lot about one of them called "The Great Train Robbery." He wanted our movie to be like that.

Their enthusiasm was contagious and all the horses, especially me, were eager to get started. Perhaps George was going to help me fulfill my dream to do something great and become famous after all.

PINTO!

At one point, George disappeared for several days. The men said he went to a large city called "Seattle." When he returned, he was even more excited than was typical for him. As he showed the other men postcards and calendars that he had printed bearing our picture, he told them about a magazine that was willing to help pay for the trip. "*The Westerner* is going to back us. All we have to do is sell subscriptions as we go across the country. We get to keep the money from the sales to cover our expenses."

The other men whooped and hollered and danced around. I just cocked my head and watched.

CHAPTER 3

The Journey Begins

The day for which we had been preparing, finally arrived: May 1, 1912. I know the date because George, Slim, Fat, and Jay were always talking about it as though it was going to be something magical. George arrived at the barn first and started tying the packs on my back the way the men had practiced so many times. Soon, Slim, Fat, and Jay joined George. A woman, who I later learned was Jay's wife, was with them. I noticed that she was crying. I never did learn why. Jay just kept telling her she was lucky to be the wife of a celebrity. Knowing that a celebrity is someone famous, I was very pleased to hear this.

The men saddled up their horses, being careful to keep dirt off their newly shined boots, and we all left the paddock at Shelton by mid-morning. George was leading me behind Lad. I watched Jay turn back and wave at his wife. She let out a loud wail. Holding her face in her hands, she dropped to her knees and sobbed.

I certainly didn't see anything to cry about. In my excitement, I kept trotting ahead of Lad. "Hold up there, Pinto," George said, giving a tug on my lead rope. "We have a long way to go. Don't use up all your energy on the first day."

Though it was hard, I did my best to slow down and stay beside Lad.

We trotted down the road for the next three hours, arriving in a large city called "Olympia" shortly after the sun reached its zenith. Clouds stretched thinly across the pale, blue sky as we approached an enormous and elaborate building that, I heard George say, was the state capitol. Lots of people were gathered in front of the building. A friendly man walked confidently up to us. Another man, carrying an odd-looking black box, trailed behind him. The second man was called a photographer. At that time, I didn't know that we were to see lots of those people in the coming three years.

"Welcome Overland Westerners," the first man said as he stepped up to me. He was a tall man and well-rounded, even by human standards. He wore a fancy black suit with a white shirt and tie. His shoes were sparkling and definitely not boots for wearing in a stable yard.

George jumped off Lad and went up to the man to greet him. "Governor Hay, so pleased to meet you," he said as he pumped the man's hand.

"A fine day. Yes, a fine day to start this amazing journey," the Governor said. Motioning to the crowd of people gathered around, he added, "And so many friends and family here to see you off. You must be very proud."

"Yes, we are, Governor," George Beck said. "May we pose for a picture with you?"

"Certainly, young man. It would be a pleasure. Jeffers," the Governor said, motioning to the man who had followed him out, "let's get everyone in the picture."

Jeffers scurried around, getting ready to take the picture. George lined up all the horses behind Governor Hay and mounted Lad. We all stood quite still while Jeffers held up the black box and took our picture. The flashes and pops from his camera startled me a bit, and I tossed my head in nervous frustration.

After the pictures, the Governor shook hands with the men and gave me a pat on the neck. He gave George some folded pieces of paper. "Here are letters of introduction for you to present to the Governors of Oregon, Idaho, and Montana, all personal friends of mine. Oh, and one thing. Governor Hawley of Idaho is a notorious horse trader. Don't trust him, he'll try to get this beautiful pinto off you for a song and a dance," he said as he stepped back, laughing heartily. "Now, young man, would you like to say a few parting words to your friends and families who have gathered to send you off?"

I watched George step toward the crowd of people. He began by talking about the purpose of the journey we would be on. "We're going to show the rest of the country that you can't find a better horse than those bred right here in the Pacific Northwest."

A cheer went up from the crowd.

"Now, we aren't foolish enough to think this will be easy," he continued. "Why with New Mexico admitted as a state in January of this year, and Arizona joining the Union the next month, we now have forty-eight state capitals to visit and forty-eight governors to meet."

My ears twitched as I listened to the murmurs that traveled through the crowd.

"They're crazy."

"They'll never make it."

"I 'spect they'll be back by Christmas," said one.

"You don't know George Beck if you think that," responded another.

George mounted Lad, took my rope from the Governor, and motioned to Slim, Jay, and Fat. "Time to go, boys!"

The Overland Westerners called out enthusiastic farewells to friends and family. George yelled, "One down, forty-seven to go!" as he buried his heels in Lad's flanks and yanked on my lead rope.

The crowd cheered, again.

Slim, Jay and Fat waved their Stetson hats in the air and spurred their horses. We left town at a brisk trot, heading south on the Pacific Highway. Salem, Oregon was our destination.

True to the Pacific Northwest, the fine day melted away as clouds, carried by ocean winds, rolled in. Light rain accompanied us for the next two and a half hours.

We continued until we had traveled a distance of sixteen miles. Though I was still full of energy and excitement, we stopped at Tenino to escape a thunderstorm, complete with hail and high winds.

George put all the horses in a nice, dry barn, rubbed us down and gave us hay and oats. He left to get food for himself, promising to come back and sleep in the barn with us.

However, a short time later, the owner of the barn came and, after checking on us, locked the barn doors. I jerked up my head and pricked my ears forward at the clicking sound of the lock latching.

I heard George come back and rattle the doors. I whinnied a greeting to him, but as hard as he shook the doors, he was unable to get in. I paced in my stall, concerned that I had been left in this strange barn without George. *Will we be safe without him here?* I wondered. *Where will he sleep? Will he be able to get us out?* I stewed and fretted all night, unable to sleep.

When I saw streams of light working their way through the cracks between the barn boards, I heard a click and a scraping sound. The door to the barn swung open. George and the livery man walked in. George didn't seem concerned at all as he went about feeding the five of us.

"How did you fellas sleep last night?" he said, looking quite rested. "I slept in a soft bed in a hotel."

PINTO!

I snorted loudly and stomped my right hoof.

By the third day, the excitement had worn off and I was getting a bit tired of the routine. Carrying a heavy load of gear that flops from side to side when we trot, can get pretty irritating. Add to that, the mud and slick roads we had to travel over, and I was having a hard time just staying on my feet. I slipped and slid, and even fell to my knees on occasion.

When mid-day came, we journeyed into a little town, stopping for some water, and for George to go into the post office. I was anticipating stopping for the day, but when we had to start out again, I admit, I lost my patience. I swished my tail and ground my teeth in irritation. I pulled back against the lead rope.

"Come on, Pinto," George said as he pulled on the rope attached to my halter. "We can't quit yet."

I planted my front hooves and refused to move.

Slim rode up behind me and gave me a slap on the rump with the end of his reins. This surprised me more than it hurt me, and I jumped forward. George and Lad walked off, and I begrudgingly followed.

Ray left the group and took Blaze ahead into the next town to put shoes on the horse's front hooves. The rest of us were moving along the bad roads at a slow pace.

We traveled along the Pacific Highway as it followed the Cowlitz River toward a town called Castle Rock. About four miles out of the next town, I decided I had had enough. George climbed down from Lad's back and I saw my opportunity. I jerked my lead rope out of George's hand, spun around, and galloped away. The packs bounced from side to side, scaring me, and I ran even faster as I attempted to get away from the packs, throwing in a few bucks for good measure.

"Hey! Pinto! Stop!" I heard George yell. I ignored him. I heard him running after me, but I soon left him far behind. I was heading home, and he wasn't going to stop me.

About two miles down the road, Ray, on Blaze, tried to catch up with me but I, being much younger than Blaze, outran them, even with my awkward load moving around on my back. Hearing Blaze breathing heavily, and his hooves pounding actually made me more excited and I ran faster and faster. My Arabian blood started to surge through my veins, and I decided I was a racehorse. I wanted to show my stuff.

Soon, I couldn't hear Blaze behind me, and I slowed down. I stopped to take a rest and nibble some green grass in the front yard of a farmhouse. Little did I know, but Fat had dismounted and was following me on foot. He came up behind me as quiet as a cat. I heard him just as he was about to grab my rope. I jerked my head up. Feeling pressure on my halter I started to bolt. Fat hung on while I dragged him a short distance. Finally, tired of the game, I stopped and let Fat lead me back.

Ray was mighty angry that he dropped his rifle when I dragged him, which caused some of the handle to break off. I didn't feel any remorse about the gun, but I did feel a little sad that Blaze was so tired after having to chase me. My companion horse wouldn't speak to me for the rest of the day. I nudged him with my nose and he just turned his back on me.

We spent the night out in the open during a terrible rainstorm. It came down in buckets all night.

George came to feed us our grain well before the sun was up. He found an old shed in a field nearby and put us in it without even asking permission. A few hours later, the men came to saddle up their mounts. When they were ready, George turned toward me, intending to catch me. I had a different idea. I noticed that the gate to the pasture was ajar. That was all the invitation I needed, and I ran for it.

"Slim, grab the gate! Pinto's headed straight for it," George shouted.

Slim was too late and too slow for me. I lowered my head and charged. I flew past him as though I had wings on my hooves.

Out the gate and onto the road I ran. Coming toward me were two gentlemen on horseback. I heard George yell again. "Stop that nag!"

Nag? Who's a nag? I thought. *I'm a magnificent Morab.* But the men clearly thought he meant me for they blocked my path while grabbing my lead rope. They led me back to George. That was a mistake. I didn't know George could get so mad. He took the end of my rope and hit me again and again. I was not going to put up with that. I reared up on my hind legs and whirled to one side, causing George to lose his balance and fall. I bolted for the gate again, dragging George through the mud for about nine hundred feet. When he lost his grip on my rope, I dashed up the road again. A young fellow caught me when I stopped to nibble on some grass. He led me back to George who was limping up the road in search of me. George took my lead rope and glared at me but didn't hit me this time. I guess I taught him a thing or two about how to treat horses.

CHAPTER 4

Traveling Onward

Blaze and Lad gave me a good talking-to that night.

"Pinto, we know you have a hard job, but that is your purpose. This journey isn't easy for any of us, but having you run away just makes it harder. You're young and strong. You need to do what your master asks of you without complaint. Be grateful that we are given plenty of food and water, a good rubbing down each day, and warm blankets at night. Some horses are not treated so well."

They made me feel a little ashamed of myself and I promised them I would do better. When George came to get me the next day, I nickered at him and gave him a gentle nudge with my nose. He smiled.

"Are we going to be friends now?" he said as he stroked my white nose.

I sneezed in his face which made him laugh. I never did try to run home again though I will admit that I hid from them a few times when I was turned out in a nice grassy valley in the forest or mountains.

The next few days continued to be extremely rainy and the mud in the road came up to our knees. I slipped and fell several times and the mud sucked off one of my shoes. When we reached a large town called "Vancouver," Fat talked a blacksmith into putting a new shoe on my hoof in exchange for a subscription to *The Westerner*. I guess that magazine came in handy after all.

I stood quietly while the farrier filed my chipped hoof and nailed a hot shoe on the bottom. This farrier was quite skilled and none of the seven nails he hammered in to hold the shoe hit a nerve, all of them going just inside the wall—the hard, outer part of my hoof. I had not always been so lucky in the past. If a blacksmith places the nails at the wrong angle, it can really hurt and leave me lame for days.

PINTO!

We camped on the shore of the biggest river I have ever seen. It is called the "Columbia." From where we were staked, on the grassy side of a railroad track, I could see the lights of a big city across the river. The lights flickered off the water, reminding me of the stars in the sky.

It took us a total of ten days to get from Olympia to the next capital city. To reach our destination, we had to take a ferry across the Columbia River. Then we traveled through the city I had seen from the other shore. I learned it was named "Portland." This fancy city had paved roads built for the new engine-powered horseless carriages that were becoming so popular. We saw many of the noisy contraptions on the streets as they dodged in and out and made loud beeping noises. I learned to not spook at them, though I never did learn to like them. For seven miles we walked and trotted over the brick surface of the roads. By the end, all of us horses were sore in our feet. Bill complained to me about his hocks, but Lad seemed the most tired and sore of all.

"I've never spent so much time on such hard roads," Lad said. "I think I actually prefer soft mud to those unyielding city streets." He folded his front legs and lowered himself to the ground. "I desperately need to get off my feet," he added as he closed his eyes.

Bill lay down beside him. Neither horse stood up all night.

It took us all a while to work out the kinks in our joints the next morning. Fortunately, for us, the men started out at a slow walk. We walked past stores and houses, other horses and lots of cars. This helped us all loosen our joints and muscles and move more freely.

After leaving the city, the road became much better. The weather dried up, taking the mud with it and making the going much easier. We journeyed through a wide, flat valley. On both sides of the road were lovely farms. I breathed in deeply the scents of freshly plowed fields of black soil and new green grasses waving in the breeze that carpeted the pastures. I nickered at the horses that I saw grazing and wished I could join them.

When we finally reached Salem, the capital of Oregon, the men pitched a tent on the outskirts of town. George said they were waiting for an appointment to meet Governor Oswald West. That was all well and good with us for, as we waited, we horses rolled in the long grass of a pasture. It was pleasant and refreshing, and I was greatly relieved to be free of the heavy pack, if only for a time. As I rolled, I rubbed the side of my head in the sweet-smelling grass and sighed in contentment.

Meeting the Governor of Oregon was much like meeting our first Governor except there weren't as many people gathered around to watch and no one cheered. The Governor visited with George, Charles, Ray, and Jay, and patted my neck.

"Fine-lookin' horse you have here," the Governor said.

"He certainly is," George said. "He has a mind of his own, I've come to learn, and his ideas don't always agree with mine," George added with a hearty laugh.

The Governor joined in his laugh. "Well, that can be good. Show's he's smart."

Then, he gave George a letter to present to the next Governor. He, too, cautioned George that the Idaho governor was a notorious horse trader. After pictures were taken, the men mounted up, Slim grabbed my lead and we left Salem.

CHAPTER 5

Trouble in the Mountains

After a few days of easy-going, we arrived in the foothills of the Cascade Mountains. I was feeling better about my job as a pack horse since we only had to cover about twenty miles a day and we had plenty of time to rest in grassy pastures or warm barns. The roads were actually getting dusty which is much better than muddy. George left me for hours each day to raise money by selling cards, calendars or magazine subscriptions to the townspeople. Often, he traded a calendar for my feed.

As the clouds rolled in later in the week, our luck rolled out. The men staked us at the camp and Blaze became tangled up in the rope. At first, he just jerked his leg, trying to free it from the rope. When he couldn't get his leg free, he started pulling harder and more violently. Still, the rope held tight around his pastern—the slim part of his leg just above his hoof. He fought so hard, he gave himself a dreadful rope burn.

"Stand still," Lad said.

"I can't. This rope has me trapped."

"You're only making it worse by fighting," Lad said. "Calm yourself."

"Easy for you to say. Nothing has a hold of your leg."

By the time the men returned and cut him loose, Blaze was in terrible pain. The next day he was limping badly. I felt sorry for him.

We arrived in a town called "Cascadia" on May 16, 1912. Several of the townsfolk greeted us as though they were not accustomed to seeing strangers in their town and were happy for it. Both men and women were eager to talk to the Overland Westerners about our historic trip.

We learned that we were soon to face a terrible challenge.

"It's too early to cross the mountains. The snow is still too deep," said one man.

"If you should make it over the Hackassian Pass, you'd be the first to do so in 1912."

"I wouldn't try it if I were you," one old-timer said. "I've lived here all my life. Many a man and beast has tried it this early, never to return."

This did not sound good to me, and I decided a nice, warm stall sounded much better.

George patted me on the neck. "With Pinto here, we'll make it. I'm sure of it."

I gave George a look of skepticism. If I'd had eyebrows, I would have knotted them. I snorted and shook my head instead.

Poor Blaze was still having an awful time with his rope burn. He was still limping something fierce. Fat put some axle grease on it. "There you go, Blaze, ol' boy," he said, wiping his hands on a cloth. "That should bring you some relief."

While we were grazing on the mountain grasses, a young woman came into camp. Pointing at Blaze, she said, "That's my horse! That horse was stolen from me when I was a tyke of just three years old. He got out of our pasture and onto the road. My good-for-nothing neighbors picked him up and sold him in Pendleton."

Blaze looked back and forth between the girl and Ray. After the young lady left, Blaze told me she was telling the truth. He remembered both that girl and being taken away from his colthood home.

We slept in a rat-infested barn that night. I heard the men tossing and turning and grumbling all night.

"Hey, get off me, you nasty, little vermin," Slim yelled, throwing a boot across the stall.

"Quiet down, Charles," George said. "We're trying to sleep."

"How are we supposed to sleep with rats crawling all over us trying to eat us for dinner?"

"Just ignore them," Ray mumbled.

"Oh sure. No problem," Slim said, throwing his saddle pad over his head.

I agreed with Slim. I refused to lay down in the straw as I didn't want the rats crawling over me. Lucky for me, horses can sleep standing up.

The Overland Westerners and their horses left early the next morning for the Mountain House, a cabin the men had been told about that was built by the foresters. We passed through the toll gates across the road; they were not manned as no one was expected on the roads this early in the season.

"Well, we saved twenty-five cents a head by coming early," Fat said with a smile on his face.

We arrived at the Mountain House at mid-day to find a large gang of men living there. They told George they were putting up a telephone line. They seemed friendly and offered to feed the men.

We horses were turned loose to graze along the creek. I led the other horses along the creek bed, grazing as we went along. We wandered quite far in search of sweet grass. When it was time to leave, the men spent over two hours searching for us. I had not intended to roam so far and felt a bit bad about seeing how the search had tired George so much.

The men tacked up the other horses and put my pack on my back. We rode to within a mile and a half of the snowline. This meant a continual, steep climb for nearly seven miles.

"We'll get an early start in the morning when the snow is still frozen," George told the men as they set up camp.

During the night, a beaver chewed on Slim's head. The little beast picked the wrong man to pick on. Slim jumped up shouting and threw the beaver through the air. Unfortunately, it landed on Fat, causing Fat to start shouting. The large, wild rodent scurried right between my legs. The ruckus the beaver made spooked me and I snorted and pawed the ground for the next hour. George finally left his bedroll and came over to calm me down. With his steady hands rubbing me, I finally settled and remained quiet for the rest of the night. I think it was that night that I first began loving George Beck.

We left camp well before sunrise and soon came upon the snow. Moonlight sparkled off the snow-crusted trees, but I was far too worried about what lay ahead to appreciate the beauty. With the first step into the snow, I, and I'm sure all the other horses and men, realized George had been wrong. The snow was so soft, we kept sinking down several feet with each step. We were soon in snow up to our bellies. In addition, large trees had fallen across the road during the winter and had not been cleared out yet.

"Another tree, another scramble around it," Jay said. "I'm not sure how much more of this the horses can handle."

"Just take it one obstacle at a time," George said as he examined the latest fallen tree. "Should we go around the roots or downhill around the branches?"

"I think the route around the roots is better on this one," Fat said.

It was an arduous journey and Lad, Blaze, Bill, Dick and I were shivering from both cold and exhaustion by the time we reached Fish Lake.

We, both man and horse, were filled with delight to find a cabin and barn stocked with food and hay. The people who ran the hotel during the summer left food behind when they departed in the fall, just in case anyone got stranded. The men whooped and hollered with joy while I just hung my head in relief. I felt like I was the one who was quite stranded, so I joined Lad at a pile of grass hay that George threw out for us. We were thrilled to spend the night in the cozy barn.

The second night at Fish Lake, after George put us all in the barn and filled our mangers with hay, I heard a terrible sound coming from Lad. Lad had been so hungry, he had gulped down a thick clump of hay. Now it was caught in his throat and he was choking. A gurgling sound was coming from his throat and he hunched his back and arched his neck. George led Lad out of the barn, and I followed, concerned about my friend.

"Fat get the vet book out of the pack," George shouted toward the cabin. "Lad is choking."

I could tell, by the quiver in his voice, that George was worried, maybe even scared.

Fat came running up to us, leafing through pages of a book. Stopping he stabbed his finger on a page. "It says to knead the throat and give sweet oil."

Slim and Fat started rubbing Lad's throat while George ran to find some Linseed oil. As soon as

George poured some liquid from the bottle down Lad's throat, he quit gurgling and hunching his back. I sighed with relief. The men sprinkled the hay with water and put us back in the barn.

"That was a close call, old pal," George said to Lad as he patted him on the neck and ran his fingers through his mane. "Slow down when you eat." Shutting the barn door, George joined the rest of the men in the house.

A thunderstorm kept us at Fish Lake for a few days. Each day, Slim struck out to find the trail and check the snow conditions. The other men fished in the lake and read magazines they found in the house. On the last day there, Slim returned after sunset, tired and hungry.

"I don't think we can make it over the pass," he said. "The snow is at least seven feet deep and I sunk in up to my knees with each step. I can just imagine what the horses would do." He pulled his hat off his head and wiped his forehead with his sleeve. "I lost the trail at Big Lake. The blazes on the trees are hard to locate."

Blazes are marks chopped into the trunks of trees to mark a trail. We watched for them whenever we were in a forest.

"I would like to suggest that the four of us go over the snow in the morning to try to locate the trail on the other side," George said as he scratched the stubble on his chin. "We won't turn back unless we absolutely must. If we can't get through here, we'll have to go south about three hundred miles to Grant's Pass."

Slim jumped up. "That's a crazy idea. The snow will be out of here before we even reach Grant's Pass."

"But ten miles of snow, seven feet deep and softened by the rain with just a few old blazes to mark the trail is no small undertaking," argued Jay.

"Add to that, we can't stay here much longer," Fat said. "We're running out of food."

"Well, let's see what we find, tomorrow," George said, the wrinkles on his forehead deepening.

The men were gone all the next day. We had a fine day relaxing and grazing. Blaze told me his rope burn was much better and wasn't bothering him at all. We had a chance to fatten up a little by resting and eating.

When the men returned, they seemed agitated and argued quite a bit with one another as they fed us and got the gear ready to depart the next day.

"This is crazy," Slim said. "We need to stay here."

"But what will we eat?" Fat said.

"Just catch some more fish," Slim said. "We can survive on fish."

"It wasn't that easy the last time we tried," responded Fat.

"And we're getting low on hay and grain," George said.

"The horses are doing just fine grazing on the grass," Jay said, giving his horse a pat.

"All we'd need is another snowstorm to come in and we'd be done for," George said.

This seemed to convince the men and they all nodded their heads in agreement.

The men may have been tired trying to work their way through the deep snow to find a trail, but we horses, having had four days to rest, all felt ready and eager to go. We had no idea what awaited us.

CHAPTER 6

Crossing the Pass

The Overland Westerners got up in the middle of the night. I nickered at George when he came into the barn to feed us. I noticed that his eyes were red and puffy. It made me feel a little sorry for him.

Happy for the oats and hay, I ate eagerly, as I always do, while the men packed the gear and tacked up. We left the warmth of the barn to discover that the temperature outside was quite cold.

"We need this freeze to make it through the snow on the Santiam Trail," Charles said. "Hopefully it will hold the horses."

It didn't.

We reached the snow shortly after leaving Fish Lake. The men dismounted and started leading us. I was third in line, behind Lad and Blaze. Dick and Bill brought up the rear. At first, we were fine as we stepped on the crusty surface of the snow. But, before long, we were in trouble. Every fifty feet or so, one of the horses broke through the top crust of ice that covered the surface of the snow and became stuck in the snow underneath that was at least eight feet deep.

"Blaze is down," Jay said. He started pulling on Blaze's lead rope. I watched as Blaze tried to get his front legs on top of the snow, but they just kept breaking through the crust and sinking back down. Nothing the horse attempted succeeded in getting him up.

"Oh no," Slim said. "What are we going to do?"

"We need to make a ramp in the snow for him to walk up," George said.

The men stomped on the snow in front of Blaze until the poor creature was able to scramble out.

This torturous journey took us seven hours. Each horse took a turn being in the lead as the trailblazer was the hardest position and exhausting for both man and horse. As I mentioned, this often meant breaking through the ice and becoming trapped in the deep snow. I told the other horses to stop struggling and let the men dig us out. I set the example for them when it was my turn to lead. I watched patiently as the Overland Westerners stomped through the snow until they had a ramp of sorts that would allow me to get out.

The ramp building was repeated over and over for eleven miles. Soon, our trail was marked with blood as the ice crust cut our legs clear above our hocks and knees. Poor Blaze, whose rope burn had healed well during our rest, was now bleeding profusely from the reopened injury on his pastern.

At times the wind picked up, sending snow flurries into our faces. Soon, my mane and tail were stiff with ice. The snow-laden fir branches seemed to enjoy dropping their cold, white loads on our backs. Squirrels came out of their holes, looked down at us from above, and snickered. I responded by lifting my head and giving them my most fierce look. They didn't seem to care in the least.

The men were as tired as we were. They started speaking in angry-sounding voices to one another.

"I told you this was a bad idea," Slim snarled.

"What else could we do?" responded Fat. "We were running out of food."

"At least there was some grass for the horses," Slim said. "There's nothing for them here, only snow and more snow." Brushing snow off his coat he added, "The miserable stuff." I had to agree.

"We have to keep going," George said. "We can make it. It can't be much farther." The quiver in his voice contradicted his words and I knew even he had doubts.

Sadly, it *was* much farther. That was seven hours I will never forget, and I hope to never repeat.

CHAPTER 7

Nip Joins Us

We had a much easier time of it once we got over the Cascade mountains. Yet, we still faced many challenges. Traveling through eastern Oregon on our way to Idaho had its good days and its bad days. In some places, the roads were smooth and hard. In others, they were slick with mud, sending us to our knees.

One evening, a woman and young girl drove their carriage up behind us. George led all the Overland Westerners off to the side of the road in the first convenient place, so they could pass. When she got opposite Jay's horse, she hit poor Bill over the head with her whip. Bill jerked his head up in pain. The woman laughed and sent her horses trotting away.

We reached Dayville, a short time later. The men dismounted and tied us to a hitching post. As they did so, a man in some well-used coveralls approached.

"You the government men my wife passed on the road into town?" he asked.

"A woman in a carriage did pass us on the road," George said, taking off his hat and extending his hand, "but we're not government men. We're the Overland Westerners. We are on the longest horseback ride in history."

The man started laughing. "Millie came into town bragging about hitting the Forest Rangers' horses. Thought she'd done quite a good thing. Wait 'till I tell her she just attacked some innocent saddle pokes."

With that, we learned that the mean woman had gone around town telling everyone that she hit the government men's horses. She had mistaken us for Forest Rangers. I don't know why it would be a bad thing to be a Forest Ranger's horse. In any case, I guess not everyone knows that we are the Overland Westerners. Poor Bill complained all night about a pain above his eye.

Blaze became lame a couple of days later as we entered a town called John Day. His front right hoof hurt so terribly he could hardly walk. It was painful just to watch him take a step. Fat took him to a blacksmith who put new shoes on his front hooves. Blaze limped just as badly all the way back to camp.

"Are you doing better?" I asked while nibbling on his withers to comfort him.

"No. That man didn't know what he was doing. I don't need new shoes. There's a sore in my hoof."

A short time later, Fat came back to examine Blaze's hoof. "Give me that hoof, old boy. Let me have a look at it," Fat said, lifting Blaze's hoof. "Well, no wonder you're lame. You've got a terrible sore on the sole of the hoof."

Blaze looked over at me with a look in his eye that said, "See. I told you."

Fat took out his knife and dug a hole in the sole of Blaze's hoof, releasing a lot of smelly liquid. "That should help a lot, Blaze," he said as he lowered the hoof back to the ground and gave him a pat on the shoulder.

Taking Blaze's lead rope, he took him back to the blacksmith where they removed the shoe and packed the hole with tar and hemp before replacing the shoe. By the next morning, Blaze was as good as new and much happier.

While on the road heading toward Prairie City, we were passed by an old stagecoach pulled by four horses. "Looky there, fellas," George said. "That's one of the old Concord stages with leather springs. Ain't seen one of those for quite a while. They charge ten cents a mile for the ride."

We dropped in behind the stagecoach. At regular intervals the driver swung his long whip above the horses' heads. The loud cracking noise it made sounded like a gunshot and caused the horses to break into a run. We had quite a go of it just to keep up.

The best day was the day we met Nip. Nip belonged to an old man named Mr. Goldsberry who ran the Prairie City Hotel in John Day. Mr. Goldsberry actually owned two dogs, Nip and Tuck. The moment George rode up to the hotel on Lad and dismounted, the dog named Nip ran up to George, stood on his back legs and licked George right in the face. He was large and black, and he later told me he was part Gordon Setter, a fact of which he was as proud as I am of my Arabian heritage.

Mr. Goldsberry laughed heartily. "Well, I guess you've made a new friend in young Nip."

George rubbed Nip on the back with both hands. "I guess so," he said.

Nip refused to leave George's side from that moment on. When George walked into the hotel for dinner, Nip went with him. When George came back to camp to feed us, Nip was right at his heels.

Later that night, Mr. Goldsberry came into camp. "I came lookin' for Nip."

"He's right here," George said. "Won't leave my side."

"So I see," Mr. Goldsberry said. "Guess the mutt wants to go with you on this crazy, cross-country journey. If that's what he wants, who am I to stop him from fame and fortune? Take him. Take him," he said, as he flipped his hands in the air as if to brush off Nip like a pesky fly.

So, from that day on, Nip was a part of the Overland Westerners. I actually learned to like the fellow. Sure, he got under foot at times. But when one of the horses stepped on him, he would just follow along on three legs until he was healed. He even managed to catch some jackrabbits and bring them back for the men to eat. This came in especially handy during the times when the men had not had anything to eat for quite a while. At those times, it was Nip who saved the day. He also became my co-star in the western shows. He loved to pose for pictures sitting on my back. I didn't know how long he would last on this long journey, but I vowed to enjoy his company for as long as it lasted.

CHAPTER 8

Goodbye Bill and Dick

While I was happy about gaining a new friend, I had no idea I was about to lose two old friends—friends with whom I had already been through many hard times.

As we neared the capital of Idaho we paused to rest. I noticed George shuffling through his pack. He pulled out a cream-colored envelope. I recognized it as the letter that the last governor had given him in Salem. I watched as he opened the envelope and pulled out the letter it contained.

"Hey fellows, listen to this letter." My ears perked forward as I listened to him read the letter.

STATE OF OREGON

Executive Department

SALEM

Hon. James H. Hawley
Governor of Idaho
Boise, Idaho
My dear Governor,
This will introduce to you Messrs J. B. Ransome, George W. Beck, C.C. Beck, and Raymond Rayne, citizens of the State of Washington, who are making a horseback trip throughout the United States with the intention of winding up in San Francisco sometime during the Panama Exposition.

Anyone who has the ability to stick to a saddle-horse is entitled to the kindest consideration at the hands of the Governor of Idaho. It is likely that they will need new horses by the time they reach Boise and may want to make a trade. I would ask that you not forget that you are the chief executive of the great State of Idaho, and no longer in the horse-trading business, as of old. Otherwise, they might suffer at your hands.

I bespeak for the boys your kindly consideration and assure you that any favors extended to them will be appreciated by their many friends.

Yours sincerely,
OSWALD WEST, Governor

PINTO!

"Forewarned is forewarned," I heard George say as we walked along a dusty, dirt road, headed toward Boise, Idaho.

"Then I say we don't ask Governor Hawley for help finding horses," Jay said as he gave Bill a hard kick to try to make him keep up. "Let's see what we can find outside of town."

"Dick's not going to make it much farther with these saddle sores," Slim said. "I say we find two new horses."

My ears twitched, and I looked back at Bill and Dick as they plodded along, their heads down, eyelids hooding their eyes. I knew the men weren't happy with Bill. He had become increasingly lazy, though he wouldn't tell me why. Maybe he was just getting old and tired. Dick, on the other hand, really was suffering from an ill-fitting saddle that was rubbing his back raw on either side of his withers. He told me it was all he could do to keep from bucking his rider off. A fine horse sure can be ruined by tack or harness that doesn't fit or a bit that is too harsh. I wish horses got to design their own saddles and bridles. Instead, we must put up with whatever our masters see fit to put on us.

Before long, we came upon a horse ranch with trading stock. We went into the barnyard. Immediately, Nip was greeted by the local ranch dogs and they took him off to hunt for rabbits. The five of us horses were greeted with nickers from horses in several corrals.

A tall, thin, older man, wearing dirty denim jeans and a long-sleeved plaid shirt, stepped out on the wooden porch of the ranch house. The screen door banged shut behind him. "You boys need some help?" he said, switching a piece of straw from one side of his mouth to the other.

"We're the Overland Westerners," George said with a warm smile. "You've probably heard of us."

The rancher pushed back his hat and scratched his head. "Naw. Caint say's I have."

"Well, you will soon enough," Slim said.

"So what kin I do for you Overland Westerners?" Mr. Personality said.

"We need to swap out a couple of these great horses," Slim said, dismounting from Dick.

"What's the matter with 'em?" the rancher said, stepping off the porch and strolling up to us. I noticed that he was looking at me the whole time, but I'm pretty used to that.

"Nothin's the matter with 'em," Slim said defensively, as he lifted his chin and placed his fisted hands on his hips. "They've just been on the road since May first. It's been a hard journey."

"And we still have a long way to go. We need some fresh horses," George added, dismounting from Lad.

"I'll make you a deal for that one," the rancher said, pointing to me.

George stepped over to me and stood beside my head. "No. He's comin' with me. But," he said, motioning to Dick and Bill, "we have these two that we need to trade."

The old man frowned as he walked around Bill and Dick, looking them up and down, checking their teeth and eyes. "Okay. I think we can make a deal on this one," he said, motioning to Bill.

Jay went to the corral and picked a bald-faced bay who seemed friendly enough and looked to be healthy. "How about a swap for this one?" Jay said.

"You give me ten dollars to cover the wear and tear on yours and we got a deal."

While George engaged the rancher in friendly talk of weather and southern Idaho ranching, Slim and Jay continued looking over the trading stock. They finally selected a buckskin with a black stripe down his back. I noticed that Slim had not unsaddled Dick, so the old man didn't know about the saddle sores.

"Will ya trade me my dependable Dick for this old buckskin?" Slim asked.

"You'll have to come up with quite a bit o' cash for that deal," the rancher said.

"What?" Slim said. "Don't you know what a deal you'd be gettin'? Why this is a famous horse. He's been ridden by the Overland Westerners. Not many people can say they have a horse ridden by the Overland Westerners."

With enough talking, the rancher was convinced that he was getting a great deal and a straight-across trade was made.

Bill and Dick watched us leave and whinnied a "farewell." While I never felt as close to them as I did Blaze and Lad, I was still sad to leave them behind.

George called out loudly to Nip who immediately lifted his nose off the trail of a jackrabbit and ran to join us.

As we rode out the gate, Slim, sitting proudly on his new buckskin, said, "I don't figure I flim-flammed him too much. After all, given a bit of a rest, saddle sores will heal."

Perhaps this is a good time to explain a bit about horses. Most humans think we are herd animals, but we really aren't. Rather than forming into herds the way cattle and buffalo, and even deer and elk do, we form bands. Bands are small groups of three to a dozen horses, like human families. Sometimes we are related, but not always. That is why horses brought together in a barn, or like Bill, Dick, Lad, Blaze and me on our journey, will band together and take care of one another. Sure, it takes a little negotiating to establish our hierarchy in the band, but we eventually get it worked out. If there should be a large group of horses, whether wild or domesticated like myself, grazing in a great open field and a threat of danger should present itself, we horses rarely stampede as one body. Rather, each band will run off in a different direction like the rays of a star. We find this to be an effective way to get away from danger. So, you see why I was sad to leave Bill and Dick behind. Our band was being broken up and new horses put in their place. The negotiations for leadership start all over again. That is hard for horses.

Over the course of the next three years, the Overland Westerners sold or traded off, or suffered the loss of sixteen horses. I, being number seventeen, was the only one that George refused to get rid of even though I was the one most people offered to buy.

CHAPTER 9

A Star is Born

Boise was the birthplace of my career as a show horse. It happened that we arrived at the local livery stable at the same time as a Wild West traveling show. The horses from the show were situated in the stalls right next to ours. I watched the men and women from the traveling show talk to George and the Overland Westerners. There was much laughter and merriment as they visited and shared stories.

"You didn't really try crossing the Cascades in early May, did you?" one man from the show said.

"Yep," Slim said.

"You don't look that stupid," the man said, pounding Slim on the back.

While our masters were getting acquainted, I took the opportunity to visit with the old mare stabled in the tie-stall next to mine. I'm sure that she was once quite a beauty, but now her gray dapples had faded and been replaced by tiny brown spots, relegating her to the title of a "Flea-bitten" gray. Her master was the founder of "The 101 Wild West Show," named after their home ranch in Oklahoma. Since 1906, the mare named Star had traveled with the show. Because there were so many traveling wild west shows—a man named Buffalo Bill being the head of the most famous one—Star's master, Mr. Zack Miller, decided to take his show across a vast ocean to a land called "England." While they were in England, that land's military confiscated most of the show's horses, stagecoaches and automobiles to help them prepare for an approaching war.

"They didn't take me because I was too small and already showing signs of age," Star said with a snort.

Mr. Miller took what little remained of his show across a narrow channel of water and began touring in other countries with minimal success.

"It is hard to put on a fancy show when most of your horses and equipment are gone," Star said, swishing a fly off her croup with her long tail.

They traveled to a land called "Germany."

"Some men in light grayish-green uniforms burst into our tent one night," the mare said, her eyes dewy wet with sadness, "and arrested many of our Oglala Sioux Indian performers, claiming they were Serbian spies. We never saw or heard from them again."

"Our owner, Zack Miller, frantic to save the rest of his performers and horses, left that night to Norway," Star continued. "Eventually, and with much difficulty, he secured passage on an American ship back to the United States." Star stopped speaking for a time while she munched on her hay.

Curious, I prodded her for more information. "And what happened when they came back?" I asked.

"Since that time," Star concluded, "we have been roaming around the country, putting on shows wherever people will have us."

Star had just finished her story when George and the man named Zack Miller came up to my stall.

"Here's the horse I was telling you about," George said as he rubbed the white blaze on my face.

"He's quite a beaut," Mr. Miller said. "You sure you don't want to sell him?"

"Not a chance. He's goin' with me the whole way," George said.

I really liked hearing him say that.

"Then I have another idea," Mr. Miller said, slapping George on the back. "How 'bout you two ride in my show while we're in Boise?"

George perked right up with that. His eyes got big and a smile filled his face. "Sure thing," he said.

That night, having been bathed and brushed until my coat nearly glowed like the moon, I found myself in a large tent filled with people seated around the edge of an oval ring. A band was playing loudly at the opposite end of the tent. George spurred me on, and we galloped around and around as people whooped and hollered, cheered and clapped. George turned me into the center of the arena and had me back up, then spin on my hindquarters until I was dizzy. When I came to a halt, George twirled his lasso over his head until it formed a big circle around the two of us.

"Ladies and Gents, I am George Beck of the famous Overland Westerners," George said in his loudest voice. "We are making the longest horseback trip in history. We will be riding to every state capital in the greatest country on Earth, the United States of America."

The people cheered.

"We'll finish up at the Panama-Pacific International Exposition in San Francisco on June first, 1915."

Another cheer from the audience.

"You can be a part of history. My companions are standing outside with souvenir cards and calendars that can be purchased to help us on our way."

The music started playing again as he gathered up his rope. I picked up my head, lifted my tail, pricked my ears, and pranced out of the tent. That was the night I decided being a show horse was a lot better than being a pack horse!

CHAPTER 10

Steep, Rough Roads

The Governor of Idaho was just as the men feared...a real horse trader if I ever saw one. A Stetson hat covered his head. He had thick hair growing over his upper lip, a strange look that some men seemed to prefer. Out of the corner of his mouth hung one of those burning, smelly brown sticks. It jiggled up and down as he talked and all he could talk about was me. He went on and on about what a fine animal I was and how he could fetch a pretty penny for me. He even insisted on holding my lead rope for the picture in front of the capitol. I didn't trust him and stayed as far away from him as I could.

Thankfully, George would have nothing to do with trading me off. "I'm sure pleased that you like Pinto," George said. "But I've grown quite attached to the little beast. I'm planning on taking him the whole way if he's able."

The next several days were spent in the mountains and canyons of Idaho as we worked our way north to a state called "Montana." I remember one particularly beautiful night in those mountains. We were staying over at a sheep ranch in the Willow Creek Mountains. The two men who lived there and worked the ranch took all of us in. The Overland Westerners spread their blankets on the haystack then went into the house. I heard music coming from the cabin until late at night. I didn't mind. The sky was as clear as a mountain lake and the moon was so bright it lit up the entire barnyard and the cliffs that loomed all around us. The only distraction was the dozen or so pigs that snorted all night as they snuffled around the hay. Sometime during the night, the music stopped, and the men came out to join the pigs on the haystack.

The next morning, the sheep farmers sent us off with a handshake for the men and a slap on the rump for me.

"You'll be headin' up Patterson Creek as it flows through the canyon for about eight miles. Keep your wits about you. The creek is running fast and high," one of the ranchers said.

PINTO!

I flicked my ears at the sound of this. Little did I know that "fast and high" was an understatement.

The road through the canyon was the worst we had yet been on. I was constantly stumbling over sharp rocks. But that wasn't the worst of it. In many places, the creek was flowing over the road so swift and deep that it nearly washed me off my feet. Our dog companion, Nip, had it the worst, I must say. At one point along the trail, he tried to cross the creek. The current was so strong, it pushed him a long way down the stream before he managed to crawl back to shore. He tried again, and the same thing happened. I stopped and watched as he flailed around in the water, drifting farther and farther away from us. I felt my heart pounding. I realized I actually liked the dog and didn't want to see him drown.

I whinnied, trying to encourage him. I kept my eyes glued to his wet head as it bobbed up and down in the rapidly moving water, and held my breath as he struggled back to the opposite shore. This time, he ran to a different spot on the creek, leaped from the shore and landed by a large rock. He scrambled up to the top of the boulder and plopped down on his belly to rest. I whinnied at him again. "You can do it, Nip. Just a little farther," I said.

Nip stood and looked down at the creek from the top of the huge rock. He lifted his head and looked at me. He responded with a whine. "I think I've got it, this time," he said while trying to suck in a lung-full of air.

With wide eyes, I stared at him as he crouched. In one swift movement, he pushed off the boulder and landed with a splash in an eddy where the water was swirling in a circle, but the current was not as strong. With his head above water, he paddled to the shore and dragged himself up the bank. He collapsed with a huff right at my feet.

Coming out of the canyon we chanced upon a camp of men charged with building the road. I wanted to tell them I wasn't very impressed with their work, but I kept my thoughts to myself and the other horses. The workers seemed grateful for the company and offered the Overland Westerners some food. As for me, I was just glad for a rest.

Late in the afternoon—I heard Fat say it was four o'clock— we left the camp and men behind and struggled up the steep road toward the top of the ridge. About a mile before the summit, the road ended, and we were forced to follow a single-lane pack trail. I was breathing heavily and grateful when George stopped all of us at the top.

"Let's stop here for a picture," he said. "I've never seen a view like this."

I was too tired to appreciate the views of the canyon and the Rocky Mountains. I was fully aware of where the Rocky Mountains got their name and I didn't much like them one bit.

Once we finished taking pictures, our troubles only continued. Before the day was through, I looked back and wished George had taken more pictures, so tired was I from struggling up and down the steep trails, trying to keep the pack balanced on my back.

CHAPTER 11

The Railroad Trestle

The trails can get not only tiring but boring as well. Fortunately, we had Fat along and Fat loved to sing. He sang both long and loud. He loved the songs titled, "Seein' Nellie Home," and "It Rained All Night the Day I Left."

The song Fat sang most often went like this:

> *"There is a boarding house,*
> *Three miles away,*
> *Where they have ham 'n eggs,*
> *Three times a day;*
> *Oh, how them boarders yell,*
> *When they hear that dinner bell,*
> *Oh, how them onions smell,*
> *Three times a day."*

I heard it so many times, I have it memorized. I bounced my head in rhythm as he sang.

Fat had a way of keeping everyone laughing. Laughter is an odd sound that men make when they are happy. Horses don't do that.

We entered a tiny town called Lombard by crossing over the mountains on a narrow sheep trail. The town is surrounded by high cliffs, so no roads have been built to get into town. There is a railroad track that passes through and the railroad is why the town is there. Here is where tragedy nearly struck my friend Lad.

The Overland Westerners set up camp for the night and turned us loose to graze on the grasses beside the railroad tracks. I didn't much like the sparse forage where we were. I lifted my head and noticed that there was lush, green grass on the other side of a narrow river. While the banks of the river were too steep for me to go down, I noticed that the railroad tracks went across a short bridge. I walked over to investigate. The steel train tracks went down the middle of the bridge. There were gaps between the railroad ties through which you could look down and see the river. I didn't dare step there. But, to one side of the steel tracks, long planks of wood were placed, forming a narrow but passable walkway.

PINTO!

I lowered my head and placed one hoof on the planks. They seemed sturdy enough, so, with only a little hesitation, I took another step. Still safe. Step, by cautious step, I worked my way over the bridge and was soon happily eating the sweet grass. Blaze saw me go and followed, as did the bald-faced bay and the buckskin. They had a little bit of trouble until they got all four hooves securely on the planks.

Lad had been foraging a bit of a distance away when he must have noticed that we were no longer with him. He jerked his head up and started calling out to us. I answered with a loud whinny. Lad started galloping around, whinnying and searching for me. I called out again. This time, he spotted me across the river and ran head-long onto the bridge. He didn't pay attention to the walkway I had used and, within a few feet, fell between the railroad ties. He was pinned between the wooden ties and the metal guard rail, his legs dangling in the air above the river. Poor old Lad was frantic. He started whinnying in fear.

I watched from the far side as George ran up. "Whoa, boy. Easy boy," he said, trying to keep his voice calm. "Jay! Slim! Fats! We need some help here. Get some help!" George shouted, the calmness gone from his voice.

Soon, the Overland Westerners had gathered several men to help get Lad out. There were ten men in all. At the same time, they sent some children to watch both sides of the track for approaching trains. Deciding I couldn't be of any help, I dropped my head and returned to grazing. I did notice that the men placed ropes under Lad's belly and across the top of the train trestle to lift Lad up high enough to get his hooves on a board. With a great deal of grunting and groaning, the men got Lad off the bridge. The poor horse was quite banged up. Streams of bright, red blood ran down all his legs. One of his hind shoes was ripped off.

We stayed where we were for two days to let Lad's injuries heal. After that, he felt good enough to head out on the trail again.

Once back on the trail, we came upon a large, beautiful ranch called Clarkston. I am sad to say that it was at this ranch that we left Lad behind. I still miss that horse to this day. Lad had been a good and wise friend to me. He often gave me counsel that has helped me become a better horse. I already mentioned the scolding he gave me when I kept running off. In addition, he was the horse who taught me to stand still while being tacked up and mounted on the occasions when George rode me. He taught me to be patient when tied to a stake, so I wouldn't get a rope burn like Blaze. Though his life had not been easy, he took all his challenges and jobs with a wonderful attitude. Before we left the ranch, I promised him I would try to become more like him.

Both George and Slim traded horses with Mr. Clark. George's new horse, while not as wise as Lad, was quite a beauty, and George had to promise to send the rancher seventy-five dollars as well as leave Lad. Slim picked a black horse with a white face. George named his new horse Kit, and I grew to like him as time went on.

CHAPTER 12

How I Nearly Drowned

There was yet another time Montana proved to be a dangerous state for us. I nearly drowned while crossing the Powder River. This is how it happened.

Ray the singer, who the other men called "Fat," was always the first to cross any river we came to. He took a long pole and poked it into the water to test the depth. He plotted the course across the river and the rest of us followed.

This method worked quite well until the day we crossed the Powder River. Fat had my lead rope, as he often did when we were to cross a river. In the past, I obediently followed right behind him as he rode Blaze across the swiftly moving river. But today was different. As we approached the river's edge, I felt my pack shift just slightly to one side. Something was wrong. I knew it. Fat entered the water, his horse walking confidently. It didn't seem like there would be any problem. Yet, I became nervous. The pack wasn't right. It wasn't centered on my back the way it should be.

I stopped at the edge of the water. When Fat got far enough away to remove the slack from the lead, it jerked my halter. Still, I remained right where I was, my hooves planted on the sandy shore.

Fat must have felt the rope get taut. He turned around. "Pinto, come on, boy."

I remained in place, bracing my thick neck against the pressure the rope and halter were putting on my head.

Fat tugged on the rope. "Come on, Pinto. Ya done this a million times. Nothin' to be afraid of."

His voice was calm and should have been reassuring. It wasn't. I felt the pack slip just a bit more. I was sure the Overland Westerners had no idea, or they would have stopped to fix it.

George rode up behind me and gave me a slap on my croup with the ends of his reins.

Startled, I jerked forward until all four legs were in the water. Resigned to my task, I started walking through the river, feeling the sand sucking at my hooves and the water swirling soothingly around my legs.

We were fine until we reached mid-stream. At that point, I felt my heavy, lopsided pack slip further to one side. I stopped moving and braced my legs as well as I could, but the top-heavy pack kept rolling to the side. Before I could figure out a way to stop it, the pack pulled me over. I went completely under water. I kicked my legs but, as hard as I tried, I could not get back up. The pack was just too heavy for me.

I soon found myself completely under water. I couldn't breathe. I must admit, I panicked. I kicked my legs even harder and tossed my head, trying to get my head above water so I could get air into my burning lungs. Nothing worked, yet I kept trying. I had to. I knew if I didn't, I would lose my life. I felt my heart pounding.

I became conscious of Nip swimming around me and barking. But he couldn't help me.

As I struggled, I threw my head up above the surface of the water. A rope flew through the air and wrapped around my head just behind my ears and jawbone. It tightened, so much that I could hardly breathe. That didn't matter much, however, as my head soon went back under water. My body began being pulled. I relaxed a bit, that is to say, I quit kicking, but I kept trying to get my head up and out of the water. The pulling continued, and I felt the pushing of the water weaken. My body bumped the sandy bottom of the river and I was able to lift my head up enough to breathe. Air never smelled so good. I guess I never appreciated it until that day.

Soon, the men were beside me, slashing the Diamond Hitch that held the pack, and pulling everything off my back so I could get on my feet.

"There's a good boy, Pinto," George said, as he rubbed my neck and loosened the rope. "I thought we lost you there. Slim, you did a great job pulling him to shallow water. He owes his life to you."

While I was grateful to Slim, I felt a bit angry at all the men for not securing the pack. I could have died! I shook my entire body, sending a spray of water over all of them, threw up my nose, and marched to shore, with Nip bounding through the water right beside me. I left them all standing in the river, soaking wet, which is what they deserved.

For the next several days, I seriously considered giving up on this entire journey. Sure, I still wanted to do something great, and maybe even become famous, but I didn't want to die in the process. George seemed to sense my displeasure and tried to make me feel better by giving me extra grooming and a double serving of oats at night. That helped change my attitude, but it still took a while. Forgiving is hard!

CHAPTER 13

A Thief

Our troubles in Montana were still not over.

One night, we camped on a rancher's property outside of Helena. I was glad for the rest and rolled in the long, waving grass. I roamed off, leading the other horses to the far end of the pasture where a little stream meandered past. The cool water felt great on my sore hooves and tired muscles. Summer in Montana was hot and dry, and the air was filled with mosquitos. I didn't like those little pests at all. But the stream provided some much-needed relief.

The men left for town in a noisy horseless carriage they called a "Depot Car." They were carrying calendars and cards to sell in Helena.

When they returned, George was talking excitedly about meeting up with the man who had been the fire chief before his retirement.

"Can you believe it? The old man showed me some famous paintings by 'Cowboy' Russell," George said.

"Who's Cowboy Russell?" Slim asked.

"Only the most famous painter in the whole country," Jay said.

"The whole country?" Slim said. His raised eyebrows and cocked head showed me he wasn't convinced.

"Well, one of the most famous, and certainly the most famous in the West," George said. George was quite taken by the paintings he saw, and described them as depicting the Wild West we had been traveling through all these long days.

Fat returned a short time later. His face was drawn with disappointment at his failure to sell many calendars or cards. After being turned down by the rich people, he said his only sale was to a poor, old, Negro lady. "That shows who are the good people in the world," he said, slapping his Stetson hat on his thigh. "The poor people every time for me."

They were unable to get an appointment for a picture with the governor until Monday. This being Saturday, we horses all breathed a sigh of relief. We were going to get a few days of rest. Monday was when trouble hit.

George was always concerned that the Overland Westerners look presentable. He didn't want to look like a bunch of out-of-work cowpokes with nothing better to do than just ride around the country. He made sure they were always bathed, and the horses and tack clean, when we went to meet a governor. With my black and white spots, I was always a standout.

It was just past dawn when I saw George leave the warmth of his blanket. "Time to get up and get presentable, boys," he said, shaking Slim out of his bedroll. "We're going to meet the governor today. There's sure to be lots of people at the capitol."

None of the men complained as they left the camp to find a private place to wash up in the creek. While they were gone, a strange man, leading a saddleless and bridleless horse, came into camp. I knew by the way his eyes shifted quickly as he looked around our camp that he was up to no good.

I was right. He immediately started sifting through the saddles and bridles, turning them every which way as he examined them. I snorted and tossed my head, but he ignored me. He grabbed a saddle pad and a saddle that I knew belonged to Blaze. He threw them up on his horse's back. At this point I started whinnying. I wanted the men to come back. I looked around for Nip but there was no sign of him. He was probably off hunting jackrabbits. I kept whinnying, hoping either Nip or George would hear me.

"Shut up, ya old nag," the man shouted.

Me? An old nag? Who did he think he was? Didn't he know a Morab when he saw one? I whinnied even louder.

But with as much ruckus as I was making, he didn't stop, and neither Nip nor George returned in time to catch the thief. Quick as a flash, the stranger had Blaze's bridle on his horse. He swung a leg over the saddle, kicked his horse's sides, and galloped out of camp. I watched him go, wondering how he had come to have a horse with no saddle in the first place.

The moment the men returned, looking clean and smelling nice, their jovial joking and slapstick antics stopped. They noticed the overturned saddles and quickly discovered that one was missing.

"My whole outfit is gone," Fat cried, his brows knitted tightly. "Everything but my chaps, is gone! What happened here? Who could have taken it?"

"Maybe one of the ranch hands just borrowed it," George said, patting his arm.

"I'll go check," Slim offered.

Slim came back a short time later. The sad look on his face told me that the man I watched take Fat's tack was not one of the ranch hands. I didn't think he was.

"The ranch hands don't have it," Slim said. "We should report this to the police when we go into town. Maybe they will know something."

I wished I could tell them what I knew.

When the Overland Westerners returned from town, they searched all the outbuildings and alfalfa fields on the ranch. I watched them with sad eyes, knowing they wouldn't find Fat's gear.

Later that night, a young man came into our camp and told us that one of his horses had been stolen. Now I understood how the thief had come to have a horse with no saddle. I don't like the evil side of some men.

George and Fat had a hard time getting a new saddle for Blaze. They had little money, certainly not enough to buy a saddle. With much effort, they were able to convince a man named F. J. Nye, who ran the saddlery in town, to give them new gear and take a chance on ever getting paid sometime in the future. I watched as Fat took his black camera that he called a "Kodak," his tent, and a pistol, and gave them to the saddle maker for security.

Blaze looked quite nice in his new tack. I was a bit jealous, but glad he had a saddle that felt good on his back and a bit that was soft on his mouth.

CHAPTER 14

Trouble with Slim

I wasn't sad to see summer go because the giant clouds of mosquitos that had been eating me alive disappeared with the heat. The mosquitos attacked me all during the summer so badly, there were times I had welts all over my body.

"These mosquitos are trying to eat me alive," I complained to Nip as I tried to reach my flanks with my teeth for a good scratch.

Nip settled down on the ground and stretched out his long body. "They don't bother me none. They can't get through my thick coat," he said.

"Well you're lucky there," I said.

George stepped up to my side. "Oh, poor Pinto," he said. "These nasty mosquitoes sure do like you. I guess we have that in common. I swear

I don't have any blood left in my whole body. Don't know what they are feasting on now."

I was glad I wasn't alone in my misery. So, you see, I didn't mind seeing summer go.

Each day saw us moving farther on our journey. We finished traveling through Montana, North and South Dakota and Minnesota, watching the leaves change from green to red and gold then flutter to the ground. Of particular beauty were the golden aspens on the high slopes of the mountains. Their bright leaves danced in the breeze and sparkled in the sun. I enjoyed shuffling my hooves through the fallen leaves and hearing them make a crunching sound as I stepped on them.

We arrived in Madison, Wisconsin to meet the Governor on November twenty-fifth, 1912. I know this because George threw up his arms and shouted, "November 25th, 1912 and we're in Madison, Wisconsin. We're doing it boys! We're going to succeed."

As we trotted slowly through the streets of Madison, I heard lots of talk about a shooting that took place just a month before in a city called Milwaukee. It seems a former president of the country by the name of Theodore Roosevelt was shot as he was preparing to make a speech.

"Did you hear about President Roosevelt?" George asked his brother.

"Didn't hear nothin'."

"The folks here told me he was shot by a saloonkeeper in Milwaukee on October fourteenth," George explained. "But that's not the half of it. Seems he went ahead and delivered his speech with the bullet still in him. When he went to the hospital after the speech, the doc said if his speech hadn't been in his breast pocket, he would have died."

"That must have been some speech!" Slim exclaimed.

By this time, all the pretty red and gold leaves had been blown off the trees by the cold winds. "Time to go south for the winter," George said as soon as the picture with the Governor of Wisconsin was taken. "The ducks and geese are already there. Here we are thawing out bits and sitting on cold rumps on frost-bitten saddles. We're dumb heads, but we're going to keep on being dumb heads." He chuckled at his own joke before adding, "It must be the cold that's kept the crowds from being here to greet us."

"I hope that's all it is," Slim said. "Maybe they just don't care."

"How could they not care? We're making the longest horseback ride in history. We're going to be famous," George said.

The men laughed and slapped him on the back as they readied the gear to leave the city.

The journey had been hard on all of us, but I appreciated George's enthusiasm. Even when he went hungry or slept out in the cold on the hard ground, he kept reminding everyone in our band of travelers that we were, step by laborious step, reaching our goal. What with George's pep talks and Rays singing, the men usually kept a pretty happy attitude even in the hard times.

I do remember one night on our way to Illinois when Slim spent the night drinking with the old man who was letting us stay in his barn. By the time he came outside the man's cabin, Slim smelled of strong drink. For two days, Slim was not acting like himself. He shouted at the men and jerked his horse around something awful. I did my best to stay away from him.

On the morning we were preparing to leave, Slim didn't come out of the house with the other men. George, Fat, and Jay set about getting ready. When Slim did come through the cabin door, I could still smell the liquor as though it formed a cloud surrounding him. His eyes were red and puffy, and his mouth was formed into an angry sneer.

"You tryin' to ditch me, ain't ya!" he shouted as he made a lunge for George. I jerked back while George pushed him away. He wobbled a bit before turning on Fat, He ran over and kicked Blaze in the ribs. Blaze squealed in surprise at being attacked and Fat pulled the poor horse away. Fat's face was red as he shouted, "Slim if you ever lay a hand on me or my horse when there is a gun in reach, I'll kill you, and so help me God, I will. I've taken all the abuse from you that I'm going to take."

The air was thick with tension and I felt my body quiver all over. Even with the cool temperature, I started to sweat. Puffs of steam floated out of my nostrils and I felt my body go stiff all over.

George swung his leg over Kit's back. "I'm heading for town to get the Sheriff."

"Wait!" Slim said, grabbing George's horse's rein. "You don't need to do that. I won't do anything."

"What you need to do is lay off the booze. It's no good, my brother," said George, glaring down at Slim.

Slim dropped his head and nodded. "You're right. No more. I promise." Unfortunately for all of us, he didn't keep that promise.

.

CHAPTER 15

Heading South for the Winter

The calendar changed to a new year just a couple of weeks after leaving the capital of Illinois. This may have signified that it was a new year, yet not much else had changed other than the weather. We still plodded along the roads and trails. In fact, I heard George say we had already traveled over three thousand miles. With each new state that we entered, we still tried, sometimes unsuccessfully, to meet Governors. It seemed fewer and fewer people greeted us at the capitol buildings for our welcome. The Overland Westerners still struggled to pay the livery bills and feed themselves. They often slept in barns and haylofts or outside on the ground.

Oh, yes, that reminds me. One thing did change. The men split up on several occasions. I wondered why they did this until I heard George talking about it one day while in Kentucky.

"Jay is staying behind until he can raise enough money to get his horse and gear out of the barn. He'll meet us down the road in Greenville," he said to Fat while tightening my pack.

I looked over at Jay's horse. His head was hanging over the stall door. He didn't want to be left behind. No horse does. But what could the men do? No matter how little money they had, they always made sure the horses were fed and bedded down, even if it meant they went without food and slept on the hard ground. Now, it seemed, they didn't have enough money to pay for all of us. I felt sad for George because he seemed so discouraged. His voice was a little quieter and his eyes a little sadder. I noticed wrinkles on his forehead that I hadn't before. I nickered and used my nose to give him a friendly push from behind. He turned around and rubbed the white blaze on my nose.

"You're a silly old nag, Pinto," he said.

I knew he meant it as a compliment. He didn't really think I was an old nag. He knows I am a magnificent Morab! I gave him another nudge with my nose.

In the end, it was decided that Slim would stay with Jay and they would come together as soon as they raised the money to pay the barn bill. I was sure that Jay's horse would be much happier to have the company.

It was a long, hard ride to Dixon, Kentucky. The roads were hilly and muddy. We did enjoy the friendly people we met along the road. They were all eager to talk to us, but too poor to buy any of George's calendars or cards, though he never quit trying to sell them.

The minute the sun went down that particular day, it became severely cold and I was relieved to finally get to the livery stable run by a man named Robert Wattons. He seemed quite kind at first.

"Welcome, gentlemen. Looks like you need a place to keep your horses for the night. Am I right?" Mr. Wattons said as we entered the barnyard.

"That we do, sir," said George. "We're the Overland Westerners, you've probably heard of us."

"Can't say as I have, but you're welcome all the same."

"We have already ridden over three thousand miles. We are riding to meet every governor in all forty-eight states," added Fat, a jovial smile on his face.

"Well, ain't that a feat...if you can do it," said the barn owner.

"Oh, we'll do it alright, especially with the help of kind people like you," George said.

"And what do you want from me?" Mr. Wattons asked, his eyes narrowing.

"We sure would be appreciative of a free stabling for our three horses for the night," George said.

At this, Mr. Wattons burst out in laughter, that strange sound I mentioned earlier. "I can't run a business giving everything away," he said between guffaws.

"Perhaps you could give us a generous discount," Fat said, his voice hopeful.

Once the barn owner got control of his laughter, he smiled politely. "Why sure, boys. How about sixty cents a head for a nice, clean box stall and a manger full of the finest hay."

"Well, that don't seem like much of a discount, but seeing as it's late and our horses are tired, we'll take it," George said. "I trust that comes with a good rubdown for each horse?"

"What kind of a stable would I be running if it didn't?" Mr. Wattons said with a crooked smile.

That was the last time I saw Robert Wattons smile.

George shook his hand and handed him the reins of his black horse. Fat did the same and the two of them left for the barn. Nip, who had been stepped on by one of the horses, limped along on three legs behind them. I should mention that poor Nip really slowed us down on our ride to Dixon as he had to lay down several times due to his hurt foot. Trying to keep up with the horses on just three legs is nearly impossible.

As soon as George and Fat left to go into town to sell some cards and raise a little money, Mr. Wattons put each of us in a small, dark, dirty stall. He took off our tack but didn't check our hooves for stones. He must have forgotten about the rubdown because he didn't give us one. I didn't mind that too much, as all I could think about was the hay he promised. When the hay finally arrived in our mangers, it was not the sweet grass or alfalfa I hoped for. Rather, it was dusty and filled with weeds, and there was so little it barely covered the bottom of our mangers.

Fat's horse looked over the rough boards that separated our stalls. "Do you call this fine hay?"

"The man's a liar and a crook," George's horse, Kit said. "I can always sniff his kind out and I knew it the minute he took my reins."

The next day, Robert Wattons' true colors came out. George and Fat came into the barn to get us, a limping Nip right beside them. A large group of men had gathered at the barn to talk about our journey. George and Fat spent quite a bit of time answering questions and joking around with the men. George took me out of the stall and let some little children sit on my back. George even put Nip on my back and let people take pictures of us. My ears twitched back and forth, listening with pleasure as everyone said how beautiful I was. After quite a while, George thanked the villagers for coming and told them it was time for us to head out. George handed Mr. Wattons the dollar eighty that they had agreed to pay.

The crowd of people watched as Mr. Wattons counted the money. When he was done, he stuffed the coins in his pocket and said, "You're ninety cents short."

"What?" Fat said. "We agreed on sixty cents a horse."

"I charge ninety cents a horse and you're ninety cents short."

"Oh, Robert," said the man with the camera, "don't be such a skinflint. These boys ain't got no money."

"That ain't my fault. They owe for services rendered."

Complaints rumbled through the crowd. As the men tried their best to talk Mr. Wattons out of the additional charge, a poor little orphan boy with skin as dark as Kit's coat stepped up to George. I recognized him as one of the boys George had put on my back.

"Here you go, mister," he said, his dark eyes soft and round. "I have a nickel. You can have it."

"I can't take your nickel, young man," George said as he placed his hands on the boy's boney shoulders.

"Please, mister. I want to help the Overland Westerners."

I noticed George's eyes getting moist. "What's your name, son?"

"I'm Smith Oran," he said, puffing out his chest.

"Well, Mr. Smith Oran, I'd be right proud to use your nickel to pay Pinto's board. Mark my words, young man, there will be a time when I make good on this loan."

After going from house to house to sell more cards and calendars...the magazines didn't sell in the South, I guess no one cared about a magazine about the West...George and Fat came back and paid their ninety cents. They tacked their horses and loaded my pack, the whole time talking to the men who were still gathered in the barn. When they were ready to leave, George and Fat shook hands with everyone except Mr. Wattons.

CHAPTER 16

Traveling Through the South

By the time we left the barn in Dixon, the rain was coming down in sheets. Soon, the rain turned to snow, and we found ourselves in an all-out blizzard. The snow kept freezing to my shoes and forming a ball of ice beneath my hooves. This caused me to roll on my hooves and stumble. The other horses were having just as much trouble as I was. George and Fat kept dismounting and knocking the snow out of our hooves.

It wasn't long before we were all soaked through and shivering. We found a stable to rest in for the night and the men threw out their bedrolls to sleep on the floor. The son of J.B Price, who worked the farm came into the barn and said, "You boys needn't go hungry around this place. Follow me into town and I'll buy ya'll supper."

I could tell George was happy as he hurried out the barn door. He had a big smile on his face and he nearly hopped instead of walked. I felt content as I watched him go. I munched the hay in the manger and lowered my head in relaxation. Soon, my eyes closed, and I took a much-needed nap.

The next morning, several men came into the barn. The tallest of the men said, "Let's give the boys a good start." Each one of them gave George a coin worth twenty-five cents. The next night, the men stayed in the Grand Hotel in Madisonville. Though cold, Kentucky was proving to be welcoming and hospitable—with the notable exception of Mr. Wattons.

I remember clearly another morning in Kentucky. We were in a town called "Hopkinsville." The men returned to the barn after eating their breakfast, and prepared the horses and gear to leave. The owner of the stable, Mr. J.J. Claborne, sent a man with a camera to take a picture of us in front of his stable. As we were posing in front of the building, a skinny, little boy, with dark skin and clothing so tattered it was nothing but rags, came up to us.

"Mr. Beck, sir, would you please take me with you? I have no family and no home. I won't be a bother and I'll work mighty hard."

George, who was riding me at the time, swung down from my back and scooped the young boy into his arms. "What a mighty fine offer that is, young man. I'm sad to say we can barely feed ourselves and can't take on another mouth to feed." Looking in the boy's sad eyes, he added. "But how would you like your picture taken on the famous Pinto?"

I looked back and saw the boy's eyes light up and a smile spread across his face. George placed him in my saddle, and that's where he sat while the pictures were taken. He was so light, I could barely tell he was on my back. I carried him to the edge of town before George helped him out of the saddle and bid him farewell.

Slim and Jay had caught up with us by this time. As we started through the farmland outside of town, I listened to George share the story of the "Night Riders." "You boys ever hear of the Night Riders?" he asked the other Overland Westerners.

Slim lifted his Stetson hat and scratched his head as though trying to bring back some sort of memory. "Sounds familiar," he said.

"Yeah," said Jay. "They had a fight with the big American Tobacco Company, if I remember right."

George swung his arms wide, drawing attention to the vast tobacco fields that we were riding through. "The Night Riders were a group of tobacco planters in western Kentucky and West Tennessee. They were fed up with the low prices being paid by the American Tobacco Company and refused to sell their crops to the giant company. One of their leaders, Dr. David A. Amoss of Caldwell County, Kentucky formed a group of militant growers. They wanted all the growers to join their boycott and refuse to sell to the company. They intimidated farmers into joining them by burning down crops and buildings at night."

He pulled me to a stop and pointed toward a building on our right. "Looky there. There's a burnt-out tobacco-drying barn. I'll bet that is one of the victims of the Night Riders, right there. The largest raid of this type was here in Hopkinsville in 1907."

Arriving in Nashville, the capital of Tennessee, proved to be a disappointment. The Governor, a man named Mr. Hooper couldn't find the time to take a picture with us. So, we posed with a different man who claimed to be his secretary. But George, who always tried to find the bright side of every disappointment, said, "Let's take pictures of Nip and Pinto in front of the statues of President Polk and General Jackson and make them into postcards to sell."

Nip and I had become quite popular with the people we passed, probably because I am so beautiful. People would wave at me and ask to pet me. George always agreed, using the time to tell everyone about our long-distance journey.

"We're the Overland Westerners and we are taking the longest journey on horseback in history," he said to the people as they stroked my neck.

"What's your horse's name?" they always asked.

"This is Pinto, and he is going to travel twenty thousand miles before we finish in San Francisco. Would you like to buy a souvenir postcard of our trip?"

"Wow!" was what they said, but I didn't see them buy any postcards.

It was in this capital that we were treated to the nicest stable I have ever seen. It was called the Waldorf. The stalls were large and warm and had a deep layer of straw for bedding. The feed was dust-free, and the water was cool and refreshing. I had a good sleep that night.

It was in Tennessee that we first came across roads called "Pikes." The roads were being made to accommodate the horseless carriages that were becoming more and more prevalent in and around the big cities, especially here in the eastern part of the country. While I don't much like those noisy, smelly carriages, I have become quite used to them and they don't scare me the way they once did. Anyway, back to the Pikes. The Pikes were made with hard packed gravel and were quite smooth. The hard surface of the road does hurt my feet and legs after a while, however. That is especially true if we trot.

On the Pike leading to Franklin, we saw a pole across the road, completely blocking it.

"What's this?" Slim said as we came to a stop.

"Maybe they're fixing the road up ahead," suggested Fat.

Just then, a tall, thin, stern-looking woman stepped out of a shack near the gate. "It will cost you five cents to pass."

"But we're the Overland Westerners. Surely, you've heard of us," said George as politely as a man can speak.

PINTO!

"I ain't never heard o'ya and I don't much care who you are. No nickel, no pass," the lady said, folding her arms across her chest with a huff.

George was the only one who had any money, so he pulled out a nickel and paid the woman in order to get her to open the gate. The bar flew up into the air and scared me. I threw up my head and quickly backed away. George dug his spurs into my flanks and I responded by bolting forward, nearly unseating him. I cantered quite a long way down the road before slowing down. Only then did I realize we were far ahead of the other Overland Westerners. Only Nip had kept up with us.

It wasn't long before we reached another gate. This gatekeeper was a man in a dirty pair of coveralls and a hat pulled down over his forehead. His appearance made me nervous.

"That'll be a nickel to pass," he said. As he spoke, he opened the gate which spooked me again and I bolted through the opening.

"Hey, come back here. Ya ain't paid," the man shouted.

"Sorry, I can't stop him!" George called back over his shoulder.

George let me run until we were far out of sight. At last, he pulled me up. "Well, Pinto, that saved me a nickel, but since I have all the money, I wonder what the other boys are going to do." Then he laughed and gave me a playful slap on the neck. I never did find out what the other horses and riders did to get past the gates.

Clouds rolled in and it started to rain something fierce. A few miles farther, we came to a junction in the road. George stopped me. "Well, Pinto, in this rain, I ain't sure which road to take to get to Franklin," he said. "Which one looks good to you?"

I turned my head and looked back at him. This would have been another time to raise eyebrows if I had any.

"So, let's go this way," George said, turning me to the right. In the cold and the rain, we continued on, and on, and on, only to find out later that this road took us ten miles out of the way. By the time we reached Franklin, the other men were already there, having arrived thirty minutes earlier. We found a stable and George gave me a good rubdown to dry me off and warm me up. Once I was thoroughly taken care of, he left me with a full manger of hay and went off to eat and sleep in a nearby hotel.

The next day, we headed out on the Pike road toward our next destination, a city called Columbia. We came to five more toll gates.

George paid the first gate keeper fifteen cents to let us pass.

"I hope we don't have any more gates because we don't have any more money," he told the short, plump woman who took his money.

"There be four more gates before ya'll reach Columbia," she said.

"Four!" George exclaimed.

By the time we reached the next gate, George had come up with a plan.

"Hello there, Gate Keeper," he said as we approached.

A kind-looking, young man stepped out of the shack.

"Today is your lucky day," George said, his voice filled with enthusiasm.

"Oh, is it now? Why would that be?" said the young man, a friendly smile on his face.

"Today is the day you get to meet the famous Overland Westerners," said George as he jumped off my back and shook the man's hand, pumping it up and down vigorously.

The young man looked a little surprised and stammered out a "Please ta meet ya, I'm sure."

"You actually get to be one of the many people who will get to help us on our journey. We are riding to every state capital in the whole dang country," George said, still pumping the man's hand. "Today we're on our way to Columbia, having just met with your Governor Hooper."

I twitched my ears and tossed my head, as I knew this wasn't true. Governor Hooper hadn't met with us.

Without taking a breath, George continued. "We are headed to our next capital, Montgomery, Alabama. Governor O'Neill is expecting us. We will be telling him about all the wonderful Southerners who have been helping us on our way."

At this point, George let go of the man's hand and draped his arm around the man's shoulder. "I'm sure you want to be one of those we tell him about, don't you? All you need to do is lift that toll gate and let us pass and you'll be able to go home and tell everyone you know that you met and helped the Overland Westerners."

George stepped away from the man and reached in his saddle bag. He pulled out a postcard and handed it to the stunned young man. "Here you go, boy. Here is proof that you provided service today. You can show this card to everyone. Someday you will even be able to show it to your grandchildren and tell them the story of the day you met the Overland Westerners as they were traveling on the longest horseback ride on record."

I snorted and nodded my head. If I could have made that funny laughing sound like the men do, I would have. I did my best, but it just came out as a little nicker. In any case, George's plan seemed to work, for the young man lifted the bar and let us pass. This scene repeated itself at the next three toll gates and we arrived late at night in Columbia, having paid only one of the five tolls.

Oh, yes, I nearly forgot. At the last toll, Nip got into a terrible fight with three dogs. The mutt came out the winner and was quite proud of himself. I told him he should quit picking fights; he might lose next time. To this he simply snorted and said, "Ain't met a dog yet I couldn't beat." I really don't understand why dogs like to get in fights. It seems a little pointless to me.

CHAPTER 17

Meeting the Mules

Having arrived in Columbia, Tennessee late at night, we were fortunate to find a warm stable. George gave me a good rubdown for which I was very grateful. I felt much better once I was dried off and warm. After I was well cared for, he said, "There you go, Pinto and Kit. I'm off to find some food." He disappeared out the barn door, giving me a chance to visit with the new horses we had picked up along the way.

"Do we have a home to call our own?" the new gray gelding said. "All we've done is travel from one town to another."

"I was wondering the same thing," said a little bay that seemed to like me a lot as he always wanted to be right on my heels.

"Don't you know what we're doing?" I asked.

Both horses shook their heads, their manes flopping from one side to the other.

"We are on the longest overland ride ever! We're going to be famous."

"It doesn't seem like we're very famous," the gray said. "No one even knows who we are."

"Haven't you noticed all the pictures they take? They end up in the local papers and people read all about us," I said, feeling quite defensive.

"Then why, if we really *are* so famous, are the men having to sell those silly cards?" the bay asked.

"And most of the time, they can't even sell enough of them to earn what it takes to sleep in a human bed," the gray wisely pointed out.

I dropped my head and took a bite of hay. What more could I say? Everything they said was true. I couldn't argue. In fact, it seemed to be getting harder and harder for the men to make any money.

The next day was Sunday, our day of rest. George put me out in a corral. I walked right to the center and rolled in a patch of mud. If I could smile, I would have. George wasn't so pleased.

"Dang horse," he said. "How am I going to get you clean now?"

It turned out that this town was famous for mules. Yes! Mules! Can you believe it? These people actually like them down here. I never met a mule I liked. 'Course, I never really met a mule before I came here.

Monday morning, as we went into the town square, I was surprised to find it filled with people and mules. I mean it when I say every corner was absolutely filled with those funny-looking creatures. Their ears are much too long, and their tails are actually bare at the top. They must be awfully embarrassed by their appearance! I know I'm embarrassed they are related to horses.

It seems that every Monday a mule sale is held on the town square. I watched with amazement as people argued, and even fought, over the right to purchase one of those silly-looking creatures. People actually wanted them. I'll never understand humans.

As we were watching the confusion around the mule sale, several men approached us to talk about our journey.

"You know, fellas," one man said, leading a large, nearly black mule, "You'd find a mule to be much better suited for your travels than those there hoses."

I snorted.

George laughed. "So I hear. But these here hoses are doing just fine. Thanks anyway."

I turned my head and looked back at George where he sat on my back. I winked at him, but I don't think he noticed.

CHAPTER 18

Summer in the South

As George put it, "We ain't much shakes in the South." While this may be true, I appreciated the warmer weather. It was nice, at long last, to be able to trot along without struggling through snow or sloshing through mud.

All summer we worked our way along the dusty roads of Florida, Georgia, and South and North Carolina while working our way back north. The entire area seemed rather…how should I put this? Slow? That's it…slow. There never seemed to be much going on. Not like in the big cities in the North, that is. People just sat around looking like, as George put it, they were waiting for something to happen.

In many towns, we were the only thing happening, and we attracted large crowds of people, especially children. They all wanted to hear about our adventures, and many sat on my back to get their pictures taken. I was proud at how patient I was as children, up to six at a time, were placed on my back. I was even easy-going when they crawled under my belly or pulled my tail. For such a young horse, I'm quite remarkable.

While the people in the towns we passed through wanted to talk, they didn't want to spend, and poor George and the men had a terrible time selling their cards or magazine subscriptions. I watched as person after person refused to buy anything.

"So much for Southern hospitality," I heard Slim grumble one day as he stuffed his unsold cards back in his saddle bag.

As I mentioned before, even if the Overland Westerners had to sleep outside on the hard, and often wet, ground, they made sure we horses were well cared for. At times, when they didn't have enough to pay the barn man, they had to nearly beg on bended knee to get us all, and our tack, out of the stable. Sometimes this worked, and the livery stable owner reduced the fee or even let us go for free. But not always. The occasions where the men were out of cash seemed to be more and more frequent. Sometimes the men split up, leaving one or two behind to try to sell enough cards and calendars to raise the money needed to pay the bill. If it was a large enough town, the men disappeared from the barn for several hours and came back later with the coins they needed to get us out.

Once a kind man appeared in the barn doorway. "I'm here lookin' for a great story to tell my grandkids. I want to say I helped the Overland Westerners ride around the whole country." The man paid the entire barn bill. When he left, Slim and Fat whooped and hollered with excitement. George just breathed a sigh of relief as he flung the saddle on my back.

CHAPTER 19

Losing a Horse

I remember the day well.

We left North Carolina so early in the morning that the sun was not even up. George said he wanted to make it to Virginia before nightfall. We trotted most of the way as the weather was quite pleasant and the roads decent enough. But as the day drew to a close, our endurance ebbed. The dark began to descend upon us like a heavy cloak. The gray outlines of little buildings gave way to open, empty fields. George and the men were unable to find a stable to put us in, nor public land to camp on. With no alternatives, we kept going.

I was getting hungry and thirsty, in addition to being so tired I wasn't sure I could put another hoof in front of the other. But the new bay mare named Dolly that Jay was riding was much worse off. I heard her breathing hard as we trotted along, and even when we stopped to rest, she didn't seem to recover.

"Are you going to be alright?" I asked, nuzzling her neck.

"Yes. Just tired and hungry. I hope they stop soon."

It was late at night before we entered a small town and found a livery. The men fed us what little grain and hay the barn owner had to offer, got fresh water from the nearby river, rubbed us down, and, supposing we were set for the night, crawled into the hayloft to sleep.

Unfortunately, the grain was poor, its terrible quality only being surpassed by the dusty, moldy hay. I watched Dolly quickly eating her grain, then move on to her hay. Before long, she had finished all the feed she had been given and started eating the straw in the bottom of the stall.

"I'm not sure you should eat that," I said.

"I'm still hungry," she said, ignoring my admonition.

During the night, the wind picked up and a thunderstorm rolled in. Bright flashes of lightning gave momentary illumination to the barn, and the thunder that followed each flash shook the building, rattling the rafters until the dust fell like rain.

Between the crashes of thunder, I became aware of another sound. The mare in the stall next to me was moving around restlessly. I peeked through the gaps in the wooden wall that divided our stalls. I saw Dolly sitting on her haunches the way Nip does. Soon, she was on her side, rolling violently from side to side. She got up and swung her head toward her belly, then kicked at it with her back hoof.

"Dolly, what's the matter with you?" I asked. "I've never seen you behave like this."

"I have a terrible pain in my stomach, and I can't seem to pass any manure," she said, dropping down and rolling again.

She struggled up to her hooves with a pitiful groan. "I fear I am dying," she whispered, her eyes looking dull and sunken.

I felt my heart pounding in my chest. I didn't know what to do to help her. *George,* I thought. *I need George. He'll know what to do.*

I pawed at the ground and whinnied.

No response from the hayloft.

I whinnied again and shook the latch on my stall door.

Still no response.

I kicked at the side boards of my stall. It seemed that each time I made a ruckus, the noise was drowned out by the angry wind and rolling claps of thunder. George would never just ignore me. It was clear he couldn't hear me.

Meanwhile, Dolly continued to be in terrible distress. Her rolling became more violent as she threw her legs from side to side so hard she banged them on the walls of the stall, cutting her legs and causing them to bleed. Up, down, up, down she scrambled.

My whinnies became louder and more frantic. I felt sweat flowing down my chest and front legs. I needed to get George's attention. After a particularly loud crash of thunder, I gave it my all. In the momentary silence that followed, I let out a loud, piercing scream. Nip heard me and ran down the stairs. "Go get George," I told him. "Dolly is sick."

I heard Nip's toenails click on the wooden stairs as he dashed back up to the hayloft.

At last, I heard footsteps stomping around overhead. The sound of creaking boards told me someone was descending the stairs. The light from a lantern sent shadows bouncing along the rough wooden walls. I whinnied as loudly as I could and followed this with a snort and a bang on the stall door with my right front hoof.

"What's goin' on, Pinto?" I heard George say as he entered the aisle between the two rows of stalls. "Between you, this dog, and the storm, a man can't get a minute of shut-eye." Nip was with him, running around him in circles and barking.

He walked up to my stall, his eyes red and puffy. But I didn't have time to worry about him. I reared onto my hind legs and let out another loud whinny. Dropping to my front legs, I ran to the side of my stall that bordered Dolly's. Tossing my head, I looked back and forth between Dolly and George.

"Dolly? Is something wrong with Dolly?" George said as he moved to her stall.

By this time, Dolly was spread out on the straw, what little straw she hadn't eaten. Her eyes were closed, and her legs were twitching. Her stomach looked as though she was carrying a foal.

"Oh no," I heard George exclaim. He turned and ran to the base of the stairs. "Slim, Fat, Jay, come help. Dolly's in trouble."

He dashed back to Dolly's stall. At the same time, I heard footsteps shaking the hayloft, sending streams of dust and bits of straw raining down upon me. With bumps and bangs, all three men stumbled down the stairs and dashed into the barn.

"She's *colicking*...I think she's impacted. Somebody grab a hose and a funnel. Someone else grab some mineral oil and a bucket of water."

I peeked through the gap in the boards as George went into Dolly's stall. "Hey, Dolly girl," he said with a soft, soothing voice. "Not feelin' so good? Stay calm. I'm here to help you."

Dolly lifted her head a few inches before dropping it back down and groaning.

"Hurry up with that mineral oil."

I could tell by the quiver in George's voice that he was scared.

"We're comin'," said Slim as he ran down the aisle, sloshing water out of the bucket with each step.

"I don't like this, George," said Slim. "What if the oil goes down the wrong tube and into her lungs?"

"Then we lose her. But we're going to lose her for sure if we do nothing. I'm sure she's got a blockage. She'll die from that if we can't get it to move."

Slim sighed and set down the bucket. Fat handed the hose to George. Jay hung the lantern on a nail, casting a bright, yellow light over the suffering mare. I watched from the next stall as George put the end of the hose first in his own mouth then gently worked it up Dolly's nostril. I couldn't watch any longer, so I turned away.

Even with my back to Dolly's stall, I couldn't help turning my ears back to listen. I heard a lot of grunting and groaning, some of which sounded like it was coming from George. Others sounded like it was Dolly. After what seemed like a dreadfully long time, the sounds changed. I heard a gurgling sound and a wheeze. Then I heard the words I feared.

"We lost her."

A long, low whinny of mourning left my throat.

CHAPTER 20

Washington D.C.

The men didn't have the money to buy a new mount. So, with the loss of Dolly, we had to carry on without a pack horse. George had started riding me most of the time anyway, but reducing our group to just four horses meant that I was never used as the pack animal again. From that time on, each of the horses carried both a rider and some of the gear. It wasn't too bad, as the men sold off everything they could spare.

We moved on from North Carolina to Virginia. It seems easy to say now, but it wasn't so easy to actually do. My commitment to George and our joint quest for greatness continued to be strong, but the journey was still just plain hard. Day after day, we trotted on rigid pikes or sloshed through rain-soaked roads from town to town, on a seemingly never-ending search for places to stay and rest our weary hooves. Sometimes I found myself questioning the wisdom in all of this. I hoped the effort would be worth it.

The days were getting hotter, the air moister, and the mosquitos bigger and more numerous.

"I think the air is sweating as much as Pinto and I are," George said one day as he lifted his hat and wiped his forehead with his bandana. I knew what he meant as my body was drenched in sweat.

Any time we came to a water crossing, I used my front hooves to splash the water over me and George. It felt great and the feeling stayed with me for the next few miles.

The Governors in many of the states seemed to be too busy to stop whatever they were doing to get their picture taken with us. We had been lucky in Florida, Georgia and South Carolina. All three of those Governors were kind enough to pose for a picture. Each one of them made a point to make a fuss over Nip and me, the only two to make it this far.

Perhaps feeling a bit over-confident, George set his sights a little higher. It was early August 1913, and George decided we should make an unplanned visit to the nation's capital, Washington D.C., before going on to Maryland. "It would be quite a feather in our cap if the new president, Woodrow Wilson, would take a picture with us," he said.

"He probably won't be there," added Jay. "He's probably shooting pasture pool at the Burning Tree or somewhere."

"What's pasture pool?" Fat asked.

"Oh, it's just a silly game where you hit a tiny ball across a pasture and try to get it in a little hole," explained Jay.

"Well, let's see if we can meet the president," said George. Ever the optimist, he added, "Besides, I've never seen Washington D.C. and I'd like to see all those cherry trees that Japan sent us. Plus, we could see the Washington Monument. It's five hundred feet tall, if you can believe it."

I felt a shiver of excitement and energy vibrate through the men and I knew we would be taking this detour. I blew the wind through my nostrils with a snort, lowered my head, and trudged on.

As we entered the city, I saw a few horse-drawn carriages and wagons, and a few horses being ridden but I had never seen so many noisy, smelly, motor cars and trucks as I saw there. Because of this, most of the streets in this big city were covered with wood, concrete, or stone. The wood wasn't so hard on my hooves and legs, but the concrete and stone roads were.

While tied up waiting for the men to go into a large and fancy building, I chanced to visit with one of the local horses standing beside me. "I'm pleased to talk with you," I said politely. "There certainly aren't very many horses in this big city."

She released a throaty nicker at which mares are so adept. "Such has not always been the case," she said with a snort of derision as a smelly horseless carriage rattled by. "In fact, I was one of the last horses to live in the White House stables. The White House, in case you don't know, is the home of the president of this great country. Anyway, I am proud to tell you that my previous owner was President Theodore Roosevelt. He was the last president to use the stables only for horses. A fine horseman he was, I must say."

I remembered that name from the story I heard in Wisconsin about Theodore Roosevelt getting shot at a speech. "What happened to the stables?" I asked.

"Well, when my owner's time as president was up, a new man came in, the one who just left a few months ago. His name was William Taft. He moved all the horses out of the stables and turned it into a garage for those noisy, smelly contraptions."

"No!" I said, shocked.

"It's true. Every word."

"Well, that explains why there are so many of them," I said, searching up and down the streets looking for some horses. I saw a few pulling wagons of goods and one or two pulling carriages but that was all. The streets were crowded with the despicable contraptions called cars and trucks. Most of the cars were black and looked alike. At least with horses, one finds lots of variety. We are far more beautiful and not nearly as noisy. And while some people may disagree, I don't think we smell bad at all.

Before the sun moved our shadows to the east, and before the mosquitos made their appearance, George returned. The look on his face, the downturned corners of his mouth and the knotted eyebrows, told me that he had failed in his attempt to meet this man they call "the president." He gave me a pat on the neck and said, "Well, we can't win 'em all, Pinto, old boy."

Who's old? I thought.

George was fiddling with my cinch when Slim, Fat and Jay returned with a man I did not recognize. "George, come meet J.H. Davis, secretary to our senator from Washington, Wesley L. Jones," said Jay.

"Mr. Davis has kindly consented to give us a tour of the nation's capital," added Slim.

The men dashed off, without so much as a "see ya soon," and climbed into a long black car—the traitors. When they returned, a man with a camera took our picture which appeared the next day in a newspaper called "The Washington Times." George was quite pleased with that and I saw the smile return to his face and twinkle return to his eyes.

The next morning, he came into the barn carrying the paper. He opened it and held it in front of my face.

"Will ya looky here, Pinto. We made it in *The Times*. You're going to be famous for sure."

I felt my dream to do something important begin to materialize as I looked at our picture. *Maybe this is going to work after all,* I thought.

CHAPTER 21

Moving North

Somewhere along the long, rough journey—perhaps on a rocky mountain trail or all alone standing in front of a state capitol, I don't recall—I decided George's goal was my goal, too. I was going to make it to this place called San Francisco, no matter what happened. The time for second guessing and complaining was past. I determined that I would keep my eyes on the trail and my ears pointed forward. We had been on this adventure for nearly a year and a half now, and I was well muscled and strong. We had already seen several horses join our group then leave for one reason or another, not to mention Dolly dying. Nope, I was not going to be one of those. I was going to make it the whole way.

Did I mention that I would not complain anymore? Well, I wasn't perfect at keeping that vow, but I tried.

George was quite eager to get to the place he called "New England."

"I hear the leaves turn from green to red and gold, and paint a picture that takes your breath away," he said.

Fat started singing a song.

"Old New England, where the leaves turn red and gold,
With a beauty that is waiting, just waiting to behold."

"Nice song, Fat," Jay said.

"You like that? I just made it up."

"I couldn't tell," responded Jay, to which he received a slap on the back with the end of Fat's reins.

We did see some mighty beautiful scenery, and it wasn't provided only by the trees covering the hillsides. I also enjoyed the times we traveled along the coastline. I liked trotting on the damp sand and watching the skinny birds called sandpipers play in the frothy surf on their matchstick legs. Inland, we shuffled through the fallen leaves making delightful crunching sounds with our hooves, and ignored the birds perched on overhanging branches watching and scolding us.

The people were kind enough but, as George said, "…mildly suspicious of four fellows with nothin' to do but ride horseback."

Meeting Governors was another story, however. We failed in New Jersey. We failed in Connecticut. We failed in Rhode Island. Then came Boston, the capital of Massachusetts.

We walked through the crowded, narrow, winding streets of what seemed to be an ancient town. Most of the time, we rode single file with me in the lead, just to get past the carriages, wagons and cars. The stone streets were slick from the rain that refused to let up. Rain dripped down my face, dropping to the street from my lips. I was miserable.

George and Fat found a comfortable livery in which we were stabled. It felt good to get out of the rain, and George and his saddle off my back. George rubbed me down until I was nice and dry. He filled the manger with hay and provided me with a bucket of fresh water. "There you go, Pinto, ol' boy," he said as he patted my rump. "I'm heading out to get an appointment with the Governor."

I stopped chewing my hay and turned to look at him. I sensed he didn't want to fail yet again, though I didn't understand what was so special about meeting a governor. Wasn't our goal to find the pot of gold in a city named "San Francisco?"

For three days, we stayed in the nice dry stable while it continued to rain outside. George returned frequently, talking about the Governor's attempts to "…put us off," and the interesting places they visited in the meantime. The livery bill kept rising until it was eighteen dollars, and the city wouldn't let the Overland Westerners sell cards or calendars. By the third day, George came into my stall, carrying my saddle and bridle. "We can't just rot here in this expensive barn, 'ol Pinto. Time for us to go."

Slim stuck his head over the stall door. "How're we going to pay the bill?"

"The owner is a fine fellow and likes us plenty. He cut the bill in half and told us to send him the first nine dollars we find running up a hill."

Slim hooted. "Mighty fine man, indeed."

"Let's go meet Governor Foss. He promised to pose for a picture this morning," George said, as he brushed my coat until I looked ready for a parade.

PINTO!

We arrived at the steps of the capitol building at the appointed time and waited. The rain, that had let up a bit earlier, decided to return. Soaked to the bone, we stood, heads down, all by ourselves. After some time, a man came out of the building. "Governor Foss refuses to pose for a picture in the rain. Sorry, boys. No picture today."

A man from a local paper took our picture and talked to the Overland Westerners for a while. "I'll see that you get a fine write-up in tomorrow's paper," he said, shaking their hands.

"We'd be much obliged," George said as he climbed back in the saddle, the leather so soaked it stuck to his pants. "We're heading off to see the leaves in New Hampshire, now."

"Success with your journey," the newspaper man said as we rode away.

We had more failures in New Hampshire, Maine, Vermont and New York. Though, I must say, the countryside was beautiful throughout the fall months and well worth the struggle it took to travel there. The temperature was growing colder by the day, and my winter coat was not coming in as fast as I would have liked.

Pennsylvania, West Virginia, Ohio, and Michigan were all in the throes of winter when we crossed through them. The same was true with

Indiana and Kentucky, though I noticed the wind getting a bit warmer, and the snow scarcer by the time March arrived and we reached Kentucky for the second time.

Sometime during the winter, we said goodbye to a couple more horses and welcomed a couple of new ones. All the horses looked to me as their leader. Even though I was still the youngest, I was the one with the most experience and could answer their questions about where we were going and what we were doing. "We're going on the longest journey man has ever taken on horseback."

"Why?" asked one new chestnut, Saddlebred we had acquired in Ohio.

"Why? Well…George thinks we'll find a pot of gold at the end," I said, swishing my tail for emphasis.

"What good is a pot of gold?" he asked astutely, with a toss of his head that sent his long forelock over his eyes.

"Seems humans think it's valuable," I said. "And I know it pays for a lot of oats."

CHAPTER 22

The Horse Race in Kentucky

Spring was spent watching the snows melt in Indiana and the flowers pop open between the snow drifts in Kentucky. By the time we reached Mississippi and Louisiana, spring was in full bloom as we traveled the wearisome roads between capital cities. Birds were nesting in the tops of the trees, squirrels, with their long bushy tails, were chasing one another around the trunks. The air smelled delightful, full of the promise of new life to come. The Overland Westerners even seemed to feel renewed. They talked happily, pointing out interesting sights along the way.

We had long ago stopped getting letters of introduction to present to the governors. The men had to do some fast talking to even get to take a picture with the occasional governor who would consent to meet with us. It seemed these men were always busy doing very important things, or gone from their offices to campaign to get re-elected. Few consented to meet with us.

We did get to meet with Governor McCleary in Kentucky. Now that was an event I will never forget. It started out in a typical fashion with George introducing us.

"Governor McCleary," George said after dismounting and taking the man's outstretched hand, "now this is a real pleasure. We're the Overland Westerners from Washington State. We are going on the longest horseback ride in history. We're visiting all the state capitals in the Union plus Washington D.C. You're our thirty-third stop."

"Well that's a mighty interesting goal," the Governor said with a kind smile. "You know, don't you, that Kentucky is the horse capital of the country."

"So we've heard," George said. "But I'd wager none of your fancy thoroughbreds could do what this little horse has done." George smiled as he rubbed my neck.

"Maybe not, but our thoroughbreds are mighty fast," Governor McCleary said. "When horse racing started in New York in the 1800's, most of the Colonies in the northeast started outlawing betting. Kentucky was one of the few states that did not. So, with our rich bluegrass pastures and legal betting, the horsemen moved their breeding and racing operations down here."

"Is the bluegrass really all they say that it is?" Jay asked.

"Well, the horses seem to thrive on it. We think the minerals in the limestone soil are what make their bones so strong."

"The Kentucky Derby in Louisville is becoming quite famous," Fat said.

"I should say," the Governor said, "all because of a very smart businessman named Matt Winn. In 1911, Winn changed the betting system to something he calls 'the parimutuel system,' where all bets go into one pool and winners are paid out of that amount. He also lowered the minimum bet to two dollars as opposed to the previous five. It has made all the difference in the popularity of the Kentucky Derby."

The Governor walked around me, looking me over carefully. I watched him and saw the unconcealed approval in his eyes.

"So, you boys the gamblin' sort?" he said, a twinkle in his eye.

"What do you mean?" George asked.

"I am," Slim said at the same time.

"Well, I was thinking we ought to spice things up a bit," the Governor said. "How about if I get up on this little pinto here and race one of you around the capitol. First one back gets two dollars. I'll even let you pick which horse we race."

"If Pinto wins, we pay you two dollars?" George asked.

"That's right. With me as the rider, of course," the Governor said.

I could see the conflict written all over George's face. He frowned and his eyebrows knitted together. I knew what he was thinking. If I won, the men would lose two dollars and they couldn't afford that. But, at the same time, George was proud of me and wanted to show this Kentucky horseman just how good a little horse from Washington was.

"It's a deal," Slim said. "I'll race you."

The Governor climbed on my back, shifting around in the saddle to get comfortable. "Lots of saddle," he said. "I'm used to English saddles."

"These saddles serve a purpose," George said as he checked the cinch. He walked up to my head and whispered in my ear. "Win, Pinto, win."

Slim, on his chestnut Saddlebred, lined up beside me on the paved road that crossed in front of the large and elegant, domed capitol building. Slim's horse and I both jigged around a bit, feeling the same level of excitement and anticipation. This was something new for the both of us.

"Riders, are you ready?" George said.

"We are," Slim and Governor McCleary said simultaneously.

"Then GO!"

I burst forward, nearly unseating the Governor who grabbed hold of the saddle horn to stay on. I hadn't been allowed to run at a full gallop the entire trip except early on when I was trying to run away and then you can't say I was *allowed*. It felt good to have the wind whistle in my ears and feel my muscles stretching and pulling.

We rounded the corner of the building side by side, Jay's chestnut keeping up with me stride for stride. We left the hard surface of the road and galloped over the groomed grass that surrounded the back side of the building. I was impressed with the Governor now that he had his balance. He was really quite a good rider. My ears picked up the sound of people cheering us on. I didn't have time to look, however, as I needed to put everything I had into beating Slim's horse. I knew I had to keep my position as the lead horse on this journey and I couldn't have him beat me. I might never hear the end of it.

We turned the last corner and headed back to where the Overland Westerners were jumping up and down and swinging their Stetson hats in the air. I felt my heart pounding. My nostrils were flaring as I sucked in air. I lowered my head and put forth the last bit of energy I could muster. To shouts and cheers, I crossed the imaginary finish line.

The race was declared a tie and I think it really was. I'm quite sure being a racehorse is not my avenue to fame. The Governor was impressed with me anyway. More important to me was the fact that the Saddlebred would have nothing to brag about that night.

"Mighty fine little horse you have here," the Governor said as he climbed down from the saddle. "Want to sell him?"

George took the reins from the Governor. "Nope. He's comin' with me. We still have a long way to go."

PINTO!

I left Frankfort, Kentucky, heading toward Mississippi, at a slow walk, knowing I would be stiff in the morning.

CHAPTER 23

Miserable in Missouri

Crossing through Texas and Arkansas in the middle of summer made me wish for the snows of Michigan and Ohio. Bugs and heat are miserable. But that wasn't nearly as bad as our journey through a state called "Missouri."

It was September of 1914 when our journey took us from Arkansas north to Missouri.

I am sad to report it was in this state we met some of the stingiest people yet, and experienced some of the worst weather of the whole trip.

One barn owner, who I remember distinctly, had the audacity to call himself a "Westerner," even though his real name was Mr. Bowens. "Bad Man Bowens" I'd call him. We stayed one night in his barn in the town of Wheeler. I knew from the moment I laid eyes on him that he was a man not to be trusted. It wasn't his physical appearance that bothered me, though his hair was a mop of greasy black curls that hung below his ears and partially concealed his face. It wasn't the gaps between his teeth when he forced a grin, nor the scratchy voice that hurt my ears when he talked. It was something in his eyes, the way they shifted from side to side, that bothered me.

"Welcome, gentlemen," Bad Man Bowens said as we approached the barn. "Lookin' for a place to stable yer horses be ye?"

"That is the case, kind sir," said George as he hoped off my back and extended his hand. "We are the Overland Westerners, I'm sure you've heard of us."

Mr. Bowens didn't say whether he had heard of us or not, but he took George's outstretched hand and shook it once.

"We are on the longest horseback journey in history and we hope you can be of assistance," George said, smiling enthusiastically.

"And what kind of assistance be ye needing from an old-time westerner like meself?" Bowens asked, his shifty eyes narrowing.

"We hope you can follow the example of Mr. Carter in Meadville from which we have just come. That generous gentleman was willing to help our cause by housing our horses free of charge."

Mr. Bowens scoffed. "Well I ain't no fool like Mr. Carter. You'll need to pay if you want to keep your horses with me."

George's face dropped, but he quickly added, "Then, perhaps you'd be willing to let us sleep in the hayloft near our horses. We won't cause any trouble and we never light a match."

"Me barn is fer horses, not humans. You'll need to find yerself a bed in the hotel 'round the corner," Mr. Bowens growled.

But it got even worse. The next morning, when the men came to get us, they were short of money, having had little luck selling cards. On top of that, Mr. Bowens charged them an extra ten cents from what he quoted the night before. When he realized the men were short of money, he quickly grabbed the hay out of our mangers. We were forced to leave without any breakfast.

"What a cheap mug," grumbled Fat as we rode away, "and he calls himself an old-time westerner."

I proudly left a large pile of manure right in front of his barn.

The next day, in a town called Chillicothe, which means big town in Shawnee, even though it wasn't big at all, we had another terrible experience. It rained all night. It rained hard all night! We stayed in our stalls throughout the morning, waiting for the rain to let up. But it only got worse…much worse. By mid-day, the wind began to blow, and the rain came down so hard, I could see out my stall window that it was causing rivers of water two feet deep to run down the center of the street. The wind got stronger, howling like a wild, caged animal. I noticed a large tree blow over and crash down on the roof of the house next door. The entire barn shook. Pieces of roofing from our barn were ripped off by the force of the wind. I pulled my head back from the window in fear and cowered in the corner of my stall. Some of our other horses were stomping and whinnying. I tried to calm them.

"We'll be okay, friends," I said. "It seems this barn is nice and sturdy."

"I remember a terrible storm at my last home in Ohio," said the Saddlebred, who was pacing back and forth in his stall. "I nearly lost my life when a barn collapsed on me."

He started to panic. His whinny was so high-pitched, it sounded like a scream. The storm was tremendously frightening for all the horses.

The storm eased by late in the afternoon, so we and our riders made a run for it even though the slippery roads were treacherous. We headed toward a town called Trenton. But after just a couple of hours on the road, the rain started in again, almost as bad as it had been earlier. I spied an open door in a farmer's barn and headed toward it. George was happy to let me have my head and go where I wanted.

Safe inside the dry barn, George dismounted. "Good idea, Pinto," he said as he stroked my wet neck. The other men followed us and soon we were all standing in the shelter of the spacious building. George ducked out, saying he was going to tell the farmer what we were doing. He soon came back, a big smile on his face. "What luck! This barn is owned by a man named Fields. He hadn't seen us ride up, but when I told him what we were doing he said he had just been reading about us in the local paper. He said we can put up the horses and stay with him for the night…for free!"

With shouts of joy and excited chatter, the men took off our saddles and bridles, rubbed us down, and found us some hay in the hayloft. When they were done with all that, they went into the house for the evening, coming back later to sleep in the hayloft.

After sleeping in the warm, dry hayloft, the Overland Westerners were treated to a large breakfast by Mr. Fields. I was glad to find out that not every man in Missouri was like Bad Man Bowens. I was also glad that the sun returned and watched over us as we trotted off to Trenton.

CHAPTER 24

Another Near Drowning

The September days continued to be rainy as we crossed into a state called "Iowa." Our group had split up for a few days, intending to reunite in the town of Carlisle, about two days' travel ahead. When we did get back together, Fat's horse, Chester, told me about a terrible experience they had.

"Jay and Fat rode us out of Chariton, Iowa early on a Tuesday morning," Chester said. "After traveling for about ten miles, we came upon a fast and overflowing river called the White Breast River. The river was running high due to the heavy rains from the last several days and weeks. To make matters even worse, the riverbank was covered on both sides by trees with low, overhanging branches. Fences that bordered the river were completely submerged in the water. Jay and Fat stopped at the water's edge and discussed waiting for the river to lower.

"'Naw,' Fat said. 'I think we can make it. Who knows how long it will be if we wait. And we're supposed to meet George and Slim in Carlisle tomorrow.'"

At this point in the story, Jay's mare, jumped in and told me more of the story. "I knew it was a bad idea right from the start. I balked at the edge of the water, but Fat kicked me. I backed up until Jay slapped me with the ends of his reins. What else could I do but obey?

"The moment I stepped into the water, the force of the current nearly swept me off my feet. I spread my feet apart, struggling to balance myself. Once I felt more in control, I inched myself to the middle of the river. I could tell by the surface of the water that it was not as deep in the center.

"At this point, I turned my head and looked back at Chester. He and Fat were about forty feet behind us. Chester was trying to bound through the water, lifting up his front legs and pushing forward with his hind legs. After a couple of bounds, Chester lost his footing and was swept under with Fat still on his back.

"The river took them under the tree branches. I watched, terrified, as Fat grabbed the first branch he could reach. He held on with one hand while he tried his best to keep Chester's head above water.

"I could feel Jay's body grow tense. He spurred me to the bank and up to a bridge that spanned the main part of the river. Don't ask me why we didn't go there in the first place! Two men were on the bridge. Fortunately, they had a rope. They managed to loop the rope around Chester's neck and pull him to shore." A tear fell from the mare's eye.

Here Chester joined in. "I was almost done for. I was so weak, I couldn't even stand once the men got me on land. I just lay on my side for a long time."

The mare continued. "I stood by the bridge and watched the men throw the rope to Fat. He tied the rope around his body and held on as the men pulled him to shore. Fat can't swim so he was underwater nearly the whole way. He came up coughing and spitting up water.

"One of the men who saved us was named Mr. Malone. He was a kind and generous man and took us back to his home. He gave Chester and me grain and hay and took the wet men into the house and provided them with dry clothing."

Chester sighed. "That is something I do not want to repeat."

"I certainly am glad you made it through," I said, rubbing Chester on his withers. It took quite a while for my heart to stop pounding as a result of hearing such a harrowing story. All the images of my own near drowning flooded my brain and a shiver went through my body. I was relieved to have all of us together again.

Our time in Iowa ended with a successful meeting with Governor Clark in front of the Capitol building in Des Moines. He was a fine gentleman and admired me greatly, which told me he had good taste. After the photo was taken with the governor, *Homestead Magazine* took pictures of Nip and me in front of the newspaper office. The magazine people promised to put the photos in the next week's magazine. I don't know if that happened, but we did get two stories in the newspapers, a fact that thrilled George.

CHAPTER 25

A War Begins

We trotted and even cantered through western Iowa, going up and down rolling hills between fields of lush farmland. Many of the farmers in western Iowa appeared to be quite wealthy, based upon the number of automobiles they owned. This was much different from the farmers in the South that seemed to be living in dire poverty.

We crossed a wide river called the Missouri on a ferry and rode into a town called Omaha in the state of Nebraska. The year was 1914. This meant nothing to me but George, Slim, Jay and Fat seemed to think it was significant. All I knew was that we had been on a very, very long journey for a very, very long time. I had seen several horses join our group and just as many leave. My buddy Nip was still with me, a fact that pleased me. The silly, and fairly stupid, dog provided some comic relief at times and I appreciated that.

George had been looking forward to reaching this city of Omaha for several days. He was sure that returning to the "West," as he called it, would bring us more success and popularity. He expected large crowds as we entered the city. Instead, as we passed through the town, no one seemed to pay us any mind. They huddled in groups, their noses buried in newspapers, and talked to one another with high energy and frantic voices. Perhaps it was because I could not read a newspaper that I didn't know a great war had broken out across the ocean on the 28th of July 1914.

"Archduke Franz Ferdinand of Austria was assassinated and now a terrible war has started in Europe," a woman in a sunbonnet said. "Now lots of countries are joining in the war."

"How long before we are forced to join in the battle?" her companion responded.

"The British have already come over to buy every spare horse they can get their hands on," said another.

The last comment caused me to lift my head and twitch my ears. Would this affect me? Would

George sell me to go off and fight a war? I wasn't quite sure what war was but by the looks on the humans' faces when they talked about it, I was sure that it wasn't something I wanted to be a part of.

George and the other Overland Westerners didn't pay much attention to the war news until it affected them. They did two interviews with pictures for the Omaha paper. Early the next morning George went to get a paper. When he came back, his face was red with anger. He threw the newspaper down in front of Charles. "War news! War news! Nothing but war news! Not an inch about us!" he shouted as he kicked a coffee pot across the ground. "How are we supposed to become famous if the papers won't cover us!"

The next day, I chanced to meet an old horse. He lived in a field next to the livery stable. The aged gelding was standing in the shade of a tree near the fence and greeted me pleasantly.

"You just passing through?" he asked.

"Yes. I'm Pinto. I'm with the Overland Westerners. We are traveling around this entire country to become famous."

"Famous, you say? Well, that is quite a feat. I wish you luck and I hope you'll make it," he said with a swish of his tail.

"Oh, we'll make it, alright. We've already been traveling for over two years. We're nearly to the end, I suspect," I said. "Though I must say, it's a much bigger country than I ever imagined."

His eyelids hooded his milky eyes. "But haven't you heard about the war?"

"War? I've heard the humans talking about war. I don't know what that is."

The old horse became more animated. "Oh, my young colt, war is a terrible thing for man and beast. I remember when I was a young colt like you, the old horses would tell the most terrible stories about war. They talked of horses and their riders screaming in pain. They described in great detail the terrible smell of blood filling their nostrils. They tried, but always failed, to describe the pain they felt when they were shot with bullets. As for me, I have been fortunate enough to never see a war for myself. But the old horses who lived through one talked about their own painful injuries and the friends who died right in front of them. It's a terrible thing, dreadful, I might add." He paused for a moment and sighed as if deciding what to say next. With a shake of his head, he continued. "I might as well tell you; I hear there are men buying up horses all around the country and shipping them across the ocean to where the war is raging.

I doubt those horses will ever return. Let us hope they don't send you."

This much talking must have tired out the old gelding for he became quiet again and dropped his head, leaving me with my own thoughts. This was disturbing news to be sure. I thought the war only affected me because it took away the pictures and stories in the newspapers that should have been covering the Overland Westerners. Now I had something far more serious to worry about. Yet, I was sure George would never send me away to a war…would he?

CHAPTER 26

Getting to Know Mooney

The city was just beginning an annual festival called "Aksarben." It seemed rather quiet compared to other festivals I have seen humans celebrate. But who am I to say? Maybe it was because of this war.

In any case, while the men were away trying to raise some money, I had a chance to talk to Mooney, Fat's new horse. I turned my head to look over at him. He wasn't much to look at, I might add. His head was a little two big and boxy. His protruding lower lip hung down when he dozed. I noticed when I walked behind him that he was a bit cow hocked as well. But with all his physical deficiencies, he seemed to have a kind heart and I liked him from the first day he joined us.

"You seem rather sad, Mooney," I said.

"My back is aching and sore," he said. "This saddle just doesn't fit right. Fat took it to a saddlery in town, but he didn't have enough money to fix it."

"I'm sorry to hear about that, my friend," I said after taking another bite of hay.

"Such is the life of a horse," Mooney said. "I've had worse."

"You have?"

"Oh yes. I was once owned by a young cowboy who spent far too much time with the bottle. He would throw any old saddle on my back, then take off at a full gallop. I had to watch my feet to keep from breaking a leg in a gopher hole as we ran across the fields. On top of that, he was a terrible rider. He bounced around something awful and swayed from side to side. He nearly threw me off balance every time he rode. My poor back hurt far more then than it does now."

This got me to thinking that I was quite lucky to have George for a master. He was an excellent, well-balanced rider with a soft hand on the reins. And, at that time, he never turned to that dreaded bottle when he was discouraged.

PINTO!

The men came back into the barn quite late that night complaining about the few sales they made. It seems there is a big carnival in town and a man named "California Frank" had his Wild West Show there as well.

"I didn't sell a single card," said Fat, as he pulled off his boots.

"Everybody thought we were part of the Wild West show," grumbled Jay.

"Yes. I was called a 'Carnie' more times than I can count," Slim said as he slapped his leg with his hat. "And everyone is suspicious of Carnies."

George came into the barn last, looking equally discouraged.

"How'd you do, George?" asked Fat.

"Not so good. No one would listen to me when I told them I wasn't part of California Frank's band. Seems they're making quite a name for themselves all around town and it isn't a pretty name. But I did get free tickets to the show for tomorrow."

"Well, that's something, at least," Slim said as he unrolled his bedroll on the hay.

The next day they came back after attending the show saying they were not much impressed. "The show Pinto and I did in Boise was much better than that one," George said with a snort.

We left town after three days of minimal success and headed for the state capital, a city called "Lincoln." We stopped the first night in a town named "Ashland." Many people in the town had read about us and we had many visitors in the barn. The energy was palpable, and the men went to bed eager to see what the next day would bring in terms of sales. Sadly, the men came back later the next day with just as little success as they had in Omaha.

With downcast eyes and a frowning mouth, Slim said, "Everyone told me about a man that's walking on stilts from coast to coast that came through a few days before us and pinched every penny out of the people. Imagine. Walking across the country on stilts. Seems like a pretty silly thing to do if you ask me."

The kind barn owner cut our bill in half and the men mounted up with their spirits lifted just a bit.

As for me, I wanted to see the man walking on stilts. I didn't even know what stilts were, but I wanted to see them anyway.

CHAPTER 27

"Tramps on Horseback"

We were in a part of the country that is vast and open, a perfect home to strong winds. With few trees and rather flat land, there was nothing to stop its constant blowing. I remember the last day before reaching Lincoln as one that was one of the most miserable. I'm not sure I can adequately describe just how miserable. We rode into a strong wind the whole day. It was blowing so hard, I could barely catch my breath. The flying sand filled my eyes, ears and nostrils. At times I couldn't even see my companions, relying on my sense of smell to know where they were. I was quite uncomfortable all day long.

Once we reached the stable, Slim and Fat gave me and the others a good sponging off while

George told stories to the many men, women and children who flocked into the barn to meet Nip and me.

Two days later, I was treated to new shoes from a local blacksmith. Early afternoon, I trotted to meet this new governor, feeling quite fine with my newly trimmed hooves and shiny new shoes. But, once again, the governor was unavailable to meet with us. We posed for a picture by ourselves and left town.

With little money, the men made several stops at farmhouses along the way, searching for someone to feed them. Time after time, they were turned away with nothing. After the fourth or fifth rejection, a farmer said, as he spoke through a closed screen door, "You'll not find any charity along here. We have phones. We've all been called and warned to be on the lookout fer ya. Ya best just be on yer way."

Just before nightfall we came upon yet another farm. "Well, here goes. Another door slammed in my face," Slim said as he got off his horse and handed the reins to Jay.

An elderly farmer answered the door, and Slim, with hat in hand, began telling him the usual story. "Hello sir, we're the Overland Westerners, you've probably heard of us and our famous long-distance ride around the country…"

The man interrupted him and, in a thick accent, said, "My name is Albert LeSell. I came here from Germany. My family and I know what it's like to be away from home. Please come in and join us for dinner."

I watched as the kind man took our riders into his house and fed them a fine dinner. He even gave a large chunk of meat to Nip. Seeing the looks of relief on the men's faces and their words of gratitude, I realized this journey is just as hard on the men as it is on Nip and me and the other horses.

The wind continued as we worked our way to the next state. Not only was the wind strong and constant, it was clearly getting colder. In fact, at times it was bitter cold. Winter was coming, there was no mistaking that fact, and no way to avoid it. My coat was getting longer. I don't look as shiny and pretty in my long winter coat. But such is life for a horse.

By this time, our group had split up again. We rejoined Fat and Slim in Topeka, Kansas. I carried George as he and Fat went to meet with the town mayor. They asked permission to sell cards on the streets of the city. I noticed the smile on George's face when the mayor said to a policeman who was standing with him, "These men are making a ride from Hell to breakfast and I want you to leave them alone. And tell the chief, too."

George shook the mayor's hand vigorously. "You're a mighty fine man, and I thank you very much."

Our good fortune did not continue, however. The men again had little luck selling cards in Topeka nor in the many small towns we passed. As we walked past a crowd of people in one of the many nondescript town squares in the center of an equally nondescript town, I heard someone shout, "Tramps on horseback, that's a new stunt."

I tossed my head, swished my tail, and stomped my hoof in disgust.

CHAPTER 28

A Show Horse Again

For three nights in a row, we stayed in a comfortable stable while we entertained crowds of people at the Yale Theatre in Wichita, Kansas. I quite enjoyed these shows. First, they were something different from our day-after-day trotting along hard or muddy roads in wind and rain, so that would make any horse happy. Second, I must admit that I like having people cheer for me. I'm quite adorable and I like being adored.

When we joined in a Wild West show, I cantered into a circular tent as music filled the air and excitement filled my heart. I am talented at prancing to the beat of the music. I lifted my head and pricked my ears forward as the people applauded. Nip trotted into the ring beside me, darting back and forth under my belly without getting stepped on. I must add that I never stepped on Nip during our long journey though he was stepped on several times by the other horses and spent many a day running beside us on three legs.

Now, back to the shows. When the show was in a tent, George and I worked out quite a nice little routine to entertain the people. First, I cantered into the tent to the sound of the music. He shot his firearm from my back as I galloped. A loud ping rang in my ears as he hit a target. After this, he swung his lasso around my head and body as I stood on my hind legs. That was always a crowd pleaser. I dropped back to my front hooves and George dismounted. Nip leaped up onto my saddle and balanced as I trotted around the ring that was placed in the center of the tent. Everyone seemed to think Nip was quite cute. To me he was just a dog, but I must admit, we had become good friends in the two years we had been together. He had been with me since the first summer. All the other horses had come and gone, but not old Nip.

The show in Kansas, however, was in a building. I walked carefully onto a slippery, wooden stage in front of the audience. It was challenging just to keep my feet underneath me. George told stories about our journey and I just stood quietly with Nip on my back. We certainly earned our keep in that town, doing six shows a day. But even with my stunning beauty and George's great story telling, we still raised only a small amount of money, and we left the town nearly as penniless as we arrived.

A funny thing happened in one of the towns. A newspaper man made up a story about me which made me out to be even more important than I already was. He wrote in his article that a wealthy man had promised to pay the Overland Westerners a dollar for every mile I traveled if I made it all the way to San Francisco.

George let out quite a hoot when he read that. "That mysterious fellow would have to pay us twenty thousand dollars. Sure would be nice if that was true, but it ain't," I heard George say as he crumpled up the paper and put a match to it, starting a fire to heat some coffee.

"It would be nice if it were true," Fat said.

"Sure would, but I wouldn't count on it if I were you," said George. "No one ever talked to me about it. I just heard about it from someone who read it in the paper and came by the barn to meet the famous horse."

"Some newspaper man probably made it all up just to sell a few more papers," Slim said as he put on his jacket.

This story, though not true, followed us from town to town. Probably as a result of the story, more and more people wanted to meet me…more and more except the governors, that is. We still didn't have much luck meeting them.

CHAPTER 29

Mooney Gets Sick

We left Wichita and headed south toward Oklahoma. The autumn weather had become much more pleasant for travel. With winter coming on, the flies were disappearing. Those flies are really quite a bother. One thing was strange, however. I noticed an odd taste in the water each time we stopped at a drinking hole in this state.

Mooney noticed it, too. "This water bothers my stomach," Mooney complained. "It has an awful, oily taste, don't you think?"

I agreed with him, though with my sturdy constitution, it didn't seem to affect my stomach.

Sadly, Mooney kept getting worse and the grain we were fed the next couple of nights didn't help any. It was an odd mixture I had never eaten before. After a couple of days, it became apparent to me that Mooney was suffering from colic. While we were moving along the road, Mooney kept trying to lay down with Fat still on his back. Fat slapped him on the rump with the end of his reins. "Ha. Get up Mooney. Keep movin'," he'd shout. I recognized the symptoms as the same ones that led to Dolly's death. This made my heart pound with worry. I liked Mooney. He was a good, dependable horse and, on top of that, I didn't want to lose another friend.

My worst fears were confirmed when I heard Fat say, "I think Mooney's got a touch of the colic."

We stopped at the next farm and waited as Slim went into the house. As we waited, Mooney tried to lay down again. Fat hopped off him just in time to keep his leg from getting crushed. Now I was *really* worried.

Slim came out of the house with a large lump of salt. "The farmer gave me this salt. He said it will fix him right up."

"I've heard of that," George said. "Never tried it before. Guess it can't hurt none."

Slim and Fat forced the white chunk down Mooney's throat. "Now get him back on his feet," Slim said. "Keeping him moving is the best."

PINTO!

I watched, my ears twitching and tail swishing, as the two men pulled Mooney back up. Fat walked beside him as we continued down the narrow dirt road. By the time we reached the next town and checked into the livery stable, Mooney was feeling fine. He left several piles of manure on the road. He even began eating as soon as he was untacked and bedded down.

I was worn out from worrying and didn't feel much like eating. I must say, I slept well that night.

Oklahoma seems to be covered with rich farmland and the people are friendly and generous. Slim put us in another show at the Majestic Theatre in Ponca. We had three shows in one day—one in the afternoon and two at night.

"You notice all the Indians in the audience?" I heard George say after the first show. "Oklahoma has a lot of reservations. In fact, they're all over the state. Reservations are large plots of land where the Indian tribes rule themselves. They're like separate nations within our nation."

Just as he said this, an enormous man with brown skin and black hair plaited into two braids approached. His dark eyes looked me over carefully. He gave me a pat so gentle I could hardly feel it. "Huh, them people no understand," he said more to me than to the men. "Me understand, cross-um mountain, swim-um river, sleep out, cook out, all kind of storm. Hardship me understand." Turning to George, he added, "Me buy two cards."

After the last show, the manager of the theater came up and slapped George on the back. "Some local businessmen told me it was the best show they have ever seen at my house. You sure you don't want to stick around?"

We left town bright and early the next morning.

Oklahoma has only been a state for eight years, according to George. They didn't have a capitol building yet as it was still under construction. We rode up to a large building that had been a schoolhouse for their children, and met with the Governor. Mr. Cruse was a friendly man and visited with us for quite a while.

"It is so good to meet you, Governor Cruse," said George, pumping the older man's hand. "We have been riding for two and a half years. You are our forty-first state to visit on our journey."

"The pleasure is all mine, I assure you, gentlemen," the portly, elderly man said with a warm smile. "How do you like our new state?"

"It's quite beautiful, and seems to be very prosperous," said George.

"Indeed, it is," Governor Cruse answered. "Rich, fertile farmland to the north. But I must brag about our oil fields. Oil was first discovered way back in 1859, quite by accident when men were digging for salt. Since 1907, even before we were a state, we have been producing the most oil of any state or territory in the United States. And there doesn't seem to be any end in sight. Why, with Henry Ford on schedule to produce a quarter of a million automobiles this year alone, and all of them needing gasoline, we could become the richest state in the nation."

I noticed the Governor lift his chest and smile broadly.

"That's quite remarkable," George said. "But I can't imagine those automobiles ever replacing the reliable ol' horse. Especially not on the farm or in the mountains."

"We shall see, my boy," said the Governor as a car veered past, barely missing us. "We shall see."

CHAPTER 30

Troublemaking Schoolboys

We left Oklahoma City and traveled through an area called the Red Mountains in Kansas, though I heard a local man call them the Gip Hills because the water is not fit to drink. And I wouldn't call them mountains. I'd seen much bigger mountains on our journey.

As we moved along, my mouth became dry and my lips felt parched. My tongue felt like it was twice its normal size. I would probably have quenched my thirst on the bad water anyway had George let me.

The area was covered with large ranches cut up into fenced pastures. We spent much our time following cow paths and stopping at wire gates to open them, so we could pass through. The wind was blowing hard, but the sun was up, making the weather just barely tolerable for a horse.

"It feels so good to be back in the West," George said, throwing away my reins and patting me on the neck with both hands.

"Yep," added Jay, "these are our kind of people, cattle people, out-of-doors people. They know what it's like to be on their own in harsh conditions."

Fat started singing.

"In the Blue Ridge Mountains of Virginia
On the trail of the lonesome pine
In the pale moonshine our hearts entwine
Where you carved your name
and I carved mine."

"That's a new song by a singer named Manuel Romain," Fat said. "It's quite popular, but that's the only verse I know." He started singing it again. His enthusiasm was contagious and soon the other men joined in.

Around mid-day, we came upon another one of those schoolhouses where the children go during most days. There were several large boys milling around outside the building. I knew right away that these boys were up to no good. Horses can just tell. Sure enough, as I watched, one of the boys picked up a rock and threw it toward us. The large stone barely missed Slim's head.

George spurred me forward and we galloped up to the boys. I wasn't sure it was such a good idea to go closer to them. Slim, who galloped up beside us, leaped off his horse, grabbed the largest boy by the throat, and slammed him up against the building. "What do ya think yer doin' boy?" Slim said, his nose nearly touching the boy's. "Ya coulda hit my horse."

The other boys scattered, and I watched as they leaped on their own horses and galloped away. I assumed we'd seen the last of them. I was wrong.

We rode away, traveling toward the Colorado state line. Just as we crossed the state border, we saw a large group of ranchers riding toward us. My ears pricked forward, and I let out a snort as the men approached. A low growl rolled up Nip's throat.

The men stopped right in front of us, blocking the road. One of them spoke first. "You fellas wanna tell us why you're pickin' on some young schoolboys?"

Slim dismounted and stepped forward. "Is that what they told you? If so, it ain't true. Those boys nearly struck me with a rock as we were riding by, minding our own business."

"Is that so?" said one.

"That's not the story we was told," said another.

"I'm sure it's not, but that's the truth, every word," George said as he leaned forward, resting his arm on the saddle horn. "We're the Overland Westerners. We're on a twenty thousand-mile journey to visit all the state capitals. We don't have the time nor the inclination to pick fights with a bunch of schoolboys."

"Hey," said one in the back of the group. "I read about you fellas and your crazy journey."

From that point on, the tension dissipated, and the men spoke back and forth in a most congenial manner.

The ranchers pointed out the best way for us to reach Cheyenne, Wyoming, a route that took us in a northwest direction across a corner of Colorado.

"It's gettin' cold, ya best bundle up," one man said as he bid us farewell.

We reached Cheyenne on December twenty-third, a month after leaving Oklahoma City.

"It's almost Christmas," Jay said, as we entered the frontier town. "I wonder what my wife is doing. Do you suppose she's making some of her delicious gingerbread?"

"Oh, don't talk about Gingerbread! I'm hungry enough as it is," Fat said.

"Still, I wonder if she's missing me. Her letters don't say much." I noticed Jay stare off into the distance, looking at nothing in particular. I hadn't heard him talk much about his wife this whole journey, though I had seen him reading letters. The men had arranged for mail at several post offices along the way.

Just before we left Wyoming, a kind local rancher led us out to his corral. The air was crisp and cold, so much so, it stung my eyes. Dry snowflakes from the previous day's snow were blowing sideways. I felt George shiver from the cold. I knew he had sold his winter coat to pay the stable bill a couple of weeks earlier.

A large group of horses with long winter coats stood huddled together on one side of the enclosure. They lifted their heads and watched us approach, though not curious enough to leave the protection and warmth of their herd as they snuggled tightly together.

The rancher stopped at the fence. Resting a booted foot on the bottom rail and an arm over the top rail, he said, "You boys can pick any horse you want…if you kin ride 'em," he said.

"Oh, we kin ride 'em, alright," Jay said. "You don't ride for two and a half years over the land we've seen and not know how to ride."

Fat dismounted from Mooney. He stood in front of his horse and looked Mooney in the eyes, one hand on each side of the old fellow's face. "You've been a good 'ol boy, Mooney. You've earned a rest." He turned to face the rancher. "I'd be much obliged if you would let me trade Mooney. A horse with a bigger heart, you'll not find anywhere. But his back needs a rest."

So, with that, my friend Mooney found a new home in Wyoming along with the other two horses in our group. I had three new travel companions to get accustomed to and teach who the boss was around here.

CHAPTER 31

The Final Year Arrives

Fat called his new horse, "Big Brown."

About as original as my name, I thought to myself.

He worked out just fine as a mount and I actually enjoyed his company during the long, cold winter nights when we could talk to one another. Big Brown told me he had spent his whole life on the wind-swept plains of Wyoming and was not bothered by the cold, though he said he never did get used to the wind. He told me the wind never stopped. Hot or cold, sun or snow, that dreaded wind just kept blowing. My short time in southern Wyoming proved this to be true. I was glad when we turned back to the south.

We had no problems walking and trotting our way from the top to the bottom of Colorado We rode through a few short snowstorms, but with the wind at our backs we did just fine. We stopped at towns with the names of Denver, the capital where we had our picture taken, Pueblo, Walsenburg and Trinidad. I liked gazing at the rugged mountains to the west, while at the same time, hoping we wouldn't have to cross them. During the many nights spent outdoors, I watched the little white dots appear, first one by one, then in clusters, until they covered the expanse of the vast blackness of the sky. True, it was cold, but George kept me blanketed at night, and the sun came out during the day, warming us right up.

The men seemed in good spirits as we rode along. Fat kept up his singing.

"It's good to be back in the West," Fat said one day as we passed by several large ranches. I had heard the men express this sentiment several times the last couple of months. Fat dropped his reins and threw out his arms as though he wanted to embrace the whole country. "Like I've said before, these are horse people, cattle people. They're the type who know what it means to struggle."

"That's for sure," Slim said.

"You notice we never have to pay for anything out here in the West," added George. "Everyone is all too willing to share as long as we entertain them with our stories."

We crossed another milestone in our journey somewhere in southern Colorado.

"We did it, boys," George said, one crisp, sunny day as we plodded along heading toward the Colorado, New Mexico border. "We made it to 1915!"

The Overland Westerners whooped and hollered, then began sharing their favorite stories of the past two and a half years.

"And look who has made it the whole way," George said, giving me a pat on the neck. Nip looked up and whined. "You, too, old Nip," he said with a chuckle. Nip stopped to scratch, then trotted ahead in search of jackrabbits.

"Do you think he'll make it?" Slim said.

"Make what?" George answered.

"Pinto. Do you think he'll make it all the way?"

I twitched my ears again but this time I added a tail swish.

"Sure, he will," said George, a note of pride in his voice. "This horse was built for the trail. He can do anything."

"Sure wish that story about the twenty thousand dollars was true," Jay said.

"You and me both," George said.

I lifted my head and tail and walked a little prouder that day to think that George thought so highly of me.

That night, one of the new horses sidled up to me. "What was all the celebrating about this morning?" he asked.

"What celebrating?" I said.

"You know. That talk about a new year. 1915."

"Oh that," I said. "It's the year we will finally finish our historic trip. I've been hearing about 1915 since we started."

While I munched my hay, I started thinking back over the trip I had been on for so long. I had now been on this journey for two and a half years. That's more than a quarter of my life. I couldn't even remember what it was like to have a stall and pasture to call home. We never stayed in one place for more than a few days and usually it was only for one, short night. I had met more horses and seen more places than any other horse in history, I would wager. I had seen cities crowded with people and deserts void of them. I had met rich people, poor people, and everything in between. I had been patted by important people and poor, little children. I had eaten sweet grass and alfalfa in warm, cozy stalls, and rotten, moldy hay in rat infested shanties. I doubt there has ever been another horse that has seen what I've seen and done what I've done.

CHAPTER 32

The Rattlesnake Attack

The southern border of Colorado was marked by a mountain range that proved to be quite a challenge to cross. We were soon exhausted as we struggled along rutted roads covered in snow and mud. As we started to climb to the top of the pass, a bitter blizzard blasted into us. We were on a rough road called "The Scenic Highway" but it wasn't scenic for us. We were surrounded by thick clouds and flying snow. The air got so thin, I was having trouble breathing. Great puffs of steam left my nostrils with each labored breath. Ice clung to my eyelashes and whiskers. But we kept working our way up to the top of the pass which was terribly high. The men said we were at 8,790 feet. The only thing that meant to me was that it was hard to breathe and bitterly cold.

Upon reaching the top, we dropped down rather quickly and got out of the worst of the blizzard. Our descent brought us into the desert of New Mexico, one of the two "new states," as George called them. We rode into the stable yard in Raton owned by Mr. Belisle. He immediately recognized us.

"Come in, come in. It's not the most pleasant day to be out and about," the round, balding gentleman said as he stepped out of the barn. "Wait! Do my eyes deceive me or might you be the Overland Westerners?" Just as he said this, the sun came out. I took this for a good sign.

"You are correct," said George with a sweep of his Stetson hat.

"Come inside, take care of your horses," he said with a jolly laugh. "After dinner I will take you to meet Mr. Griffin, the editor of our newspaper. He'll want to do a write-up, I'm sure."

"We'd be much obliged," said George as he swung his leg over the back of my saddle in a hasty dismount.

We had a comfortable stay in Raton and George was pleased to get a nice article in their paper. The next night, George and I performed in two shows in the Lyric Theater in town. There were few people in the audience, as it seems there was a popular activity at the roller-skating rink involving skaters trying to catch a greased pig. That didn't make much sense to me. I sometimes wonder why people do what they do. But we made enough money at our show to pay the stable bill and feed the men.

We continued on our journey the next day. I noticed how dry the land looked and the odd-looking structures called "Dobes," that the people lived in. My nose frequently picked up the scent of odd smelling foods baking in ovens behind the Dobes. Sometimes the smoke stung my eyes. The men were having a hard time talking to these people as it appeared they spoke a different language, words I didn't recognize any more than the men did. I'm glad we animals don't have that problem.

We rode through a tiny village with lots of those funny houses and people we couldn't understand. As we reached the edge of the village, seventeen wild dogs dashed after us. Nip, always up for a challenge, turned and curled back his lips, showing his sharp teeth. A low growl rose up from deep inside of him.

The dogs kept coming. They were small, skinny things with battle scars all over their bodies. They looked like they hadn't had a decent meal in days. But they chose the wrong dog with whom to pick a fight. I should have warned them, I guess. They found out soon enough that Nip was not to be messed with. Watching Nip handle those mangy mutts reminded me of a hawk among sparrows. They didn't have a chance. He had all of them running away whimpering with their tails between their legs in no time. I must say, I was impressed with Nip. Seventeen to one is quite the challenge, but if any dog can hold his own and come out on top, it's Nip.

I snorted and tossed my head while the men clapped their approval.

"You showed 'em, Nip," Fat said.

That night, Nip curled up next to me and I had a little talk with him.

"Thanks for chasing those mangy dogs away," I said.

"Aw-w-w, it was nothing," he said, as he gave me a toothy dog smile. "That's my job."

"But you could have gotten hurt with so many dogs coming at you."

He shrugged. "I've been hurt before, probably will be again. It's a dog's life for sure."

PINTO!

The farther south we traveled, the lower the altitude, making it easier to breathe. Add to that, the warmer temperatures and lack of mud or snow, and we had quite an easy go of it all the way to the large town of Albuquerque. The local paper had written a nice story about our journey. As a result, many people came to see us, me especially, in the barn.

As was typical on picture day, the men spent quite a bit of time brushing us and cleaning the tack before getting cleaned up themselves. George didn't want anyone looking like a "saddle tramp"— his words, not mine. We left the barn and went to meet with the governor. After finding the building in Albuquerque that was being used as the temporary capitol, and getting our picture taken, we headed west toward Phoenix, Arizona, the other "new state." It was somewhere along this desolate trail that tragedy struck.

The open range was spread out before us. Odd-looking plants, many with sharp spines and thorns, dotted the countryside. Water holes, usually marked by a windmill, were few and far between. Each day we kept going until the sunset, sometimes going for hours without water. I once heard that Arabians were bred to gallop across deserts and go for long periods of time without water. I guess it was because of my noble heritage that I held up better than the other three horses. They all grumbled and complained about being tired and thirsty. I managed just fine. Still, I tried to encourage them.

"We'll find water, soon," I told them with a quiet nicker.

"I hope you're right," said Fat's horse. "I feel like my tongue is filling up my whole mouth and threatening to block my throat."

We all dropped our heads and let our eyelids droop as we plodded along.

One day, while the men were dismounted and eating what little food they had with them, we horses were let loose to forage around on the dry, stiff grasses. I let my whiskers tell me if I came upon something edible. Even still, whatever I came upon was a poor excuse for food, I must say. Molly, a mare that Slim had picked up in Wyoming, was grazing beside me. She was a pretty little thing, but having been born and raised on a horse ranch in Ohio, she was not much accustomed to the sparse conditions in which we now found ourselves. She moved away from me in search of something decent to eat when I heard a rattling sound. I lifted my head and turned in the direction from which the sound came. Molly heard it, too. I watched her prick her ears forward and swish her tail. Raising her muzzle just slightly off the clump of grass on which she was nibbling, she stepped forward.

"I wonder what that strange sound is," she said. "I think I'll check it out."

In one sudden flash of brown and gray, a large snake lurched forward and sunk its fangs into her nose. Molly reared back, the snake still dangling from her muzzle. Shaking her head, the snake dropped to the ground and slithered off toward a cluster of rocks.

I stepped up to Molly and noticed blood dripping from two, round puncture wounds right between her nostrils. Within a few seconds, her nose began to swell. I watched in horror as the swelling quickly moved up her face until I couldn't even recognize her. Her eyes swelled shut. Her nostrils turned puffy and red.

"I can't breathe," she whispered.

I didn't know what to do. Just then, Nip dashed by, his nose to the ground following some animal's scent. "Nip get the men," I said. "Molly's in trouble."

Nip lifted his head, took one look at Molly, and dashed off to retrieve George. I heard Nip barking at him. It seemed to take forever for the man to figure out that something was wrong. Meanwhile, the swelling was moving down Molly's neck, pinching her throat. Finally, I heard Nip, whining and yelping, returning to where we stood, as the sound of footsteps crunching on the sandy soil was heard coming behind him.

I was so relieved when George came up. Just as he approached, Molly crumpled to the ground, unable to breathe.

George dropped to his knees beside her. "No! Oh, no!" he shouted. "Slim, get over here." The urgency in George's voice must have startled Slim for he was beside us as quick as a flash of lightning.

Slim shook his head and let out a long breath. "Rattler."

"That's what I thought," George said. "The early heat must have brought them out. We need to be alert. If one's out, there will be others."

"What can we do about Molly?" Slim asked, bending over Molly's body and rubbing her with the palms of his hands.

"Ain't nothin' we kin do except put her out of her misery," George said with a shake of his head.

George got up, handed Slim a pistol, and led me away.

PINTO!

I jumped when I heard the loud bang. I felt tears stinging the backs of my eyes. I clenched my jaw and dropped my head. It took me quite a while to quit quivering.

CHAPTER 33

Meeting Kind People in Utah

With only three horses and four men, we took turns carrying the extra gear for the next couple of hours until we chanced upon a ranch house. The little structure was set far back from the dirt road and I only hoped that they would have a water trough nearby. Imagine my excitement when they did. I dipped my whole head into the cool, refreshing water, nearly to my eyes. I shook my head, splashing the invigorating water over my neck and chest. I'm not sure anything ever felt as good.

George and Slim walked up to the ranch house. It was a tiny but well-maintained clapboard building with a large porch across the front. I watched them bang on the door. A small woman in a dress made from a blue and white print fabric answered the door. Her cheeks were plump, made to look even more so when she smiled, which she was doing now.

"Hello, ma'am," I heard George say. "I'm George Beck and this is my brother, Slim…um, I mean, Charles."

"Please ta meet cha, and pleased for the company," she said. "Won't you come in and get out of the hot sun?"

"Thank you, ma'am," George said.

"Oh, call me Martha," she said, opening the door wider and letting the men enter the doorway. I watched as the men disappeared into the dark opening that led into her house.

It wasn't long before the men came back out, the little woman following right behind carrying a basket. In the basket she had carrots for the three of us horses, and biscuits for the men.

"Mrs. Walker has offered to sell us one of her horses," Slim said.

"Happy to help out you men on such a marvelous adventure," the kind woman said, her plump cheeks glowing.

And that is how our band returned to four.

PINTO!

Each day the temperature increased as we worked our way to Phoenix, the capital of Arizona. We arrived in the spread-out town of low buildings during the heat of the day and quickly found a livery stable. I was glad to get out of the sun and fill my belly with some clean, though not cold, water. I was disappointed that we didn't rest for long. The men had a photo taken in front of the capitol early in the morning of the next day. They filled leather skeins with water from a pump, mounted up, and sunk their heels in our flanks. Turning our heads to the north, we cantered out of town.

Crossing into the beautiful red rocks of Utah from Arizona was a treat for the eyes to be sure. I had never seen land like this. Red cliffs dotted with aromatic junipers rose up all around us. Green rivers of fresh water flowed beside our trail much of the way.

Fat's current horse, Miami, had become quite attached to me and didn't want to leave my side, whether on the trail or at night while eating and resting. This could get a little irritating at times, especially when he was so close that he stepped on my heels. I swished my tail to tell him to stay back a little, but he didn't pay any attention.

"Back up, Miami," or "Move over Miami," I said frequently, with a snort and a roll of my eyes. He just ignored me and stayed right where he was.

On one occasion, however, I was grateful that he was right beside me. That was the time we crossed a muddy river. Even though the water was not terribly deep, the water was so murky I couldn't see where to place my hooves. At one point, I placed my hoof down on a rock that rolled beneath my weight. This threw me to one side. Lucky for both George and me that Miami was right by my side and kept me from falling over.

Utah was dotted with small settlements of farmers trying to survive in the High Desert climate. Poor as they might be, the people were kind and generous to a fault, usually feeding both man and beast in their barns and homes. We met a forest ranger named J.V. Manwill in a town called American Fork who took us into his stable. The tall, robust man hung around and talked with the Overland Westerners until quite late at night. He had a loud laugh which he used often. (I still think that is an odd sound for humans to make.) Before he left the barn, he told the men his wife would have breakfast ready for them in the morning.

When the warm sun sent its rays into the barn, lighting up dancing dust particles, the men rose and fed us our hay. I heard Mr. Manwill call the men to breakfast. When the sun was well up in the sky, Mr. Manwill came back to the barn with the Overland Westerners and his children. Mr. Manwill placed two of his children on Lopez, Slim's new horse that replaced Molly. He placed one child in the saddle and the other, a little girl, behind the saddle. I saw Lopez's ears pin back and I knew we were in trouble. Most horses don't like pressure on their back past where the ribs can support the weight. Lopez was obviously one of those horses.

Lopez started bucking. The little girl did her best to cling to her brother, but she quickly lost her hold and went flying through the air, landing with a loud thud on the dusty ground. My heart started pounding and I held my breath as Lopez's front hooves just missed her head where she lay on the dirt. Her mother came running out of the house, the screen door banging loudly behind her. Based upon the look on her face, I was sure she was frightened for her daughter, and for good reason. I was, too.

For a moment the little girl didn't move. I kept staring at her, my head lowered. Suddenly she sat up and started making that odd laughing sound. "I'm not hurt," she said, a big grin on her face.

Her father, Mr. Manwill scooped her up and put her on my back. I stood motionless so as not to frighten her as they took our picture.

We carried the men into town where they tied us to a hitch rack while the men tried to sell cards. While they were gone, a large crowd gathered around us.

"Hey, ain't that the famous Pinto, the horse that's traveling around the whole dang country?"

"Sure is, I'd recognize him anywhere."

"He's so beautiful," said a young woman with good taste.

Just as I was enjoying the compliments, the fire alarm sounded, and the crowd rushed away toward the fire. Mr. Manwill rode his saddle horse over to the fire house and tied the two-wheeled hose cart with its tank of water to his saddle horn. He and his horse pulled it to the fire, quickly extinguishing the flames. I was quite impressed with Mr. Manwill's horse. We horses are quite afraid of fire. Yet, this horse was both brave and strong and set about his job with confidence. When Mr. Manwill brought his horse back to the hitch rack, I told the horse how impressed I was.

"Oh, it was nothing," he said. "All in a day's work for a horse."

PINTO!

We left town later that day and trotted up the road to a small village called Sandy. A kind family, immigrants from a country named "Norway," took us in and fed us well. I noticed how funny they said their words. Though I understood what they were saying, they didn't sound like George or the other Overland Westerners when they talked.

We arrived in Salt Lake City, the state capital, the next day. The men put us up at a lovely stable and the stableman said we could stay for free. While we rolled in the straw bedding and munched on our hay, the men took a tour of the city. They came back talking about how beautiful and clean the city was.

"These people are smart. They have planned out this city with wide, straight roads," George said. "Plenty of room for horses and cars."

"And they number the streets in order," Jay said. "No getting lost here."

After the sun set on the western mountains, a large group of actors and actresses from the Empress Theater came to see Nip and me. I let them feed me treats and stroke my mane. There was a lot of talking and laughing.

One of the men, a Mr. Cook, was full of energy and enthusiasm. He was the manager of the theater. He pulled George aside and said, "I regret that my theatre is closed for the time you will be in town, but I will do my best to book you in all the principal towns between here and Frisco. The manager of the concessions at the Expo is an old friend of mine. Let me cover the cost of promoting you and financing your exhibit in exchange for fifty percent of the gross receipts."

The men were so excited, they couldn't sleep all night. George went out the next day to buy new clothes to celebrate. Slim celebrated by getting drunk again and causing quite a row among the men.

"Here we finally have our big break," Fat shouted, shaking Slim by the shoulders, "and you throw it all away on the bottle."

Slim shoved Fat and stomped away. Fat made a growling sound like a dog.

The tension made me nervous and I pawed the ground. We left this lovely city with the men not even speaking to one another other.

CHAPTER 34

Crossing the Desert

The first part of our journey across the desert was spent on an old stage road, called the Lincoln Highway, that the men said ran from Missouri to California and was used by the Pony Express. I had heard of the Pony Express, the men who carried the mail across country, galloping their horses as hard as they could for a short distance before switching horses. It sounded like a tough thing to be a pony in the Pony Express. I decided I liked our slow walk and trot along the dusty roads better than an all-out gallop.

Once we hit the desert, I was surprised the area was as desolate as it was. We traveled a long way between any sign of human activity. We went through miles of sand, hard and level, heading for the promised well. The men had been advised to carry a bucket. When we reached the well, the men dismounted and loosened our saddle cinches to give us a rest. I watched, licking my parched lips, as they tied a rope to the handle and lowered the bucket. I heard the splash when it hit the water. The men quickly pulled the bucket up to the top. As they did so, a large, gray rat jumped out of the bucket. Startled, the men shouted and fell backward, spilling the water which quickly soaked into the ground.

Now rats don't frighten me. I've put up with their sneaky ways all my life as they try to steal my grain. That doesn't mean I like them. Not in the least. But I desperately wanted that water! I snorted and gave George a shove with my nose.

"Okay, okay, Pinto," George said. "We'll get more water."

Not long after leaving the well, we rode into a terrible rainstorm that quickly soaked both us and the hard ground. Three inches of water turned the desert road into slippery mud. Eventually we reached a road that followed the base of the mountains. It was cut along a slick, rocky surface and was easier going than the mud.

We traveled for twenty-five miles before we found another well. As we plodded along, dragging our hooves, I noticed a lake up ahead. I quickened my step, eager to reach the shimmering water. But, as I moved toward it, the lake kept moving farther away. I hurried my step, yet the faster I went toward it, the faster it moved away from me. I have never seen a body of water behave like this.

It must have occurred to George just what I was doing for he started laughing. "Hey fellas, Pinto sees that mirage ahead and thinks it is really water. He keeps trying to hurry to get to it. Poor fella is probably thirstier than we are."

I didn't know what a mirage was but after a time of trying to reach the water and having it just run away from me, I gave up. I dropped my head and started dragging my feet again.

By the time we finally reached the long-sought-after well, I was very weary and not sure I could take another step. The water in the well was very salty but I drank my fill anyway.

Once night fell, with no moon above us, we had quite a hard time of it. The day went from hot and wet to so cold all I could do was shiver. The men were following a light in the distance that they were sure was our destination, a place called Fish Spring. I focused my attention on staring at the light, but it never seemed to get any closer. I tried testing it. I looked away for a while. When I looked back, it was still just as far away. Watching the light got discouraging. I tried not to look, but my eyes kept going back to it.

Then, at nine o'clock, the light went out! Now, with nothing to guide us, we stumbled around for a long time in search of the waystation. It was far into the night before we reached the old stone cabin and horse corral for which we had been searching.

The land around the cabin was the strangest I had ever set hoof upon. It wobbled with each step I took. We later learned that the waystation is surrounded by springs with a thin layer of sod over the top. It was this sod that we were walking on, feeling the ground bounce as our hooves sank in. I shivered with nervousness the whole way. I felt sweat covering my neck and chest. Imagine how happy I was to be turned out in the corral and find a little shed with dry ground. I only ate a small amount of hay before laying down. I was so glad to get off my hooves. It had been a difficult and long day, one I hoped not to repeat.

I met Mr. Thomas the next morning. The caretaker of the waystation was a tall man with a well-weathered face that reminded me of an old barn door. His hair was gray and short, and stuck straight up over his head. I sensed right away that he was not a man to be trifled with, so I kept my distance. The old man lived alone at the stage house. His job was to help travelers when they needed it, for which I was grateful. We certainly needed it. But I had a hard time deciding if he was glad to have company or if he resented us disturbing his peace and quiet, viewing us as nothing but a bother.

Mr. Thomas directed us to the best pass over the mountains to our next stop, a settlement called Kallao. When we arrived, we discovered that the few families who lived in the settlement had been taking care of two automobile parties that were stuck in the mud from the previous day's rainstorm. I must admit, I got a bit of a kick out of being able to trot past them, my head up in the air. Horses really are much better than those dang motor cars, after all.

We caught up with a Mr. Kearney who, with his little daughter, was driving west to visit his family. He talked Jay into riding with him so they could talk. I think some of the people in these isolated outposts get tired of just looking at one another and welcome getting acquainted with someone new—most people except, that is, Mr.

Thomas. The Overland Westerners always had great stories to tell so they were always popular.

In any case, because Jay was in the carriage, George took off my saddle, put it in the buggy, and rode Jay's horse. I can't tell you how good it felt to trot along without anything on my back for the first time in nearly three years.

At the top of a ridge, we looked back to get our last look at the Great Salt Lake desert that we had just crossed. Far in the distance, I could just make out the buildings at the settlement and, beyond that, barely visible and sitting silently by itself, was the waystation. I wasn't sad to leave it behind. Yet, little did I know that we had an even tougher desert to cross before we reached our final state capital: Sacramento.

Going west through Nevada, one must cross more vast and daunting deserts populated by little more than gila monsters, tarantulas and snakes— that I have learned to stay far away from—and dotted with cactus and tumbleweed. We did most of our travel at night and rested during the hottest part of the day.

"This is the part of the trip I most feared and dreaded," said George one day as we trudged along, searching for a spot to get out of the sun. I knew the men were as hot and weary as I was, so

PINTO!

I didn't complain. I dropped my head and dragged my hooves but kept moving, step after step, day after day, week after week, until we reached our final capital and posed for our final picture with our final governor.

CHAPTER 35

San Francisco at Last!

I **never have** liked baths. In fact, I hate them to this day. But the date was May 31, 1915, the day before we expected to make our grand entrance into San Francisco to the sound of bands playing and people cheering. Sensing the importance of what we were about to do, and knowing how eager he was to show me off, I stood patiently while George scrubbed me all over with a stiff brush to within an inch of my life. When he was done and my coat had dried in the warm California sun, even I was impressed. My white was as pure as the new fallen snow. My black was as deep as a moonless night sky.

Nip was less cooperative. Poor Fats did his best to give Nip a bath in a large, round, metal water trough. But every time he let go, the wet, shaggy monster jumped out and ran off, shaking his body, and sending sprays of soapy foam in all directions. If I could laugh like humans do, I would have.

After traveling for 1,127 days and covering 20,352 miles, the men were showing signs of the trials of the trail. Their gaunt faces and skinny bodies were in sharp contrast to the plump ones of the governors and their representatives we met along the way. But there was no hiding the sparkle in their eyes or the excitement in their voices on this day as they prepared for the festivities to come.

The first sign that things were not to be as expected came when a letter arrived from Mr. Clark in Salt Lake City. He had been unable to secure a concession for us on the midway. It seems there was room for Little Sheva, the belly dancer, but not for four horses and their riders.

"No matter," said George, his enthusiasm unabated. "The crowds will be there, and they will love us."

Wearing the new clothing they had purchased in Salt Lake City, and carrying freshly cleaned tack, the men arrived early in the stable to feed us and give us a final brushing. Except for the fact that they were skin and bones, the Overland Westerners looked better than I had seen them at any time since the day we left Washington over three years ago.

With stomachs full of hay and hearts full of anticipation, we left the stable. George directed us up the paved roads to the west side of the city where he knew the Panama-Pacific International Exposition was located. As we approached the buildings, I noticed many cars and trucks but no horses.

"We're almost there," George shouted, unable to contain his excitement.

"Is this the way to the midway?" Fat asked.

"Yep," George said. "Right between these buildings and around a park. We'll be there soon. I'll bet people have been lined up for hours to welcome us."

We followed George's directions. Once in the park, I noticed several people, but none of them even acknowledged us, let alone cheered our arrival.

"Keep going to the midway," George said. "The crowds must be there."

We crossed the park and walked under an archway with a lighted sign that said, "Midway." George pulled on the reins and I stopped. My ears twitched back and forth. I didn't hear any music. I didn't hear any cheering crowds. One man shouted at us. "Get them hayburners off the street." That was the only one who greeted us, and it didn't sound very friendly to me. I swished my tail, but kept my hooves firmly planted on the pavement.

The men dismounted and stood silently, staring straight ahead. I read their thoughts on their faces. "Three years of our lives. Nine thousand dollars begged, borrowed and scraped up as we went along. Sleeping in rat-infested barns or out in the freezing rain and snow. Nearly starving most of the time. And all for what? Nothing. A big, fat nothing."

Jay dropped his head and spoke first. "I want to go home and see my wife…if she'll still have me."

CHAPTER 36

Returning to Bainbridge Island

In less than a fortnight, I found myself standing beside George in front of a railway station. A damp fog swallowed the steam from the engine. People hurried past, carrying luggage and waving train tickets. Nip was curled up on the wooden platform, his back pressed against my front legs.

Beside us, the Overland Westerners stood in a tiny cluster, eyes downcast, looking dejected. Slim, Fat and Jay were now horseless, saddleless, bridleless, and everything else-less, having sold anything of value they had left. With the little money they scraped up, they purchased train tickets back to Seattle.

"I wish you wouldn't give up, fellas," George said, a sorrowful pleading in his voice. "I think we can still get some gold out of the end of this rainbow. I'll sell our story to some movie producers or big-time authors like Jack London."

"Give it up, George," Slim said. "Ain't nobody cares about us or our lamebrained idea."

"Someone will. I just know it," George said, clasping Slim's arm as though he wanted to hold him there. "We've set a world record for the longest horseback ride in history."

Slim pulled away. "I'm goin' home."

George turned to Fat. "Fat, won't you stay? You have your journals. We can use those to write a book."

"George," Fat said, his eyes sad yet sympathetic, "I'm bone tired and can't go on. Face it: We did our best. It just didn't work out. The gold at the end of the rainbow sailed out to sea without us."

Fat pulled some money out of his pocket and handed it to George. "This is all the money I have left, George. Use it to get Pinto home. Don't sell him."

The train blasted its horn and the three men walked away, disappearing into one of the cars. Nip sat up and whined. George put an arm over my neck and the three of us watched the train pull away. We stood there motionless until the train disappeared in the fog.

For the next several days—I can't tell you how many as it all seems to fade into one big blur—Nip and I stayed in a barn just outside of town. George left each morning and came back at night to sleep in the straw. He always brought Nip something for dinner, though I never saw George eat.

One night he returned to the barn looking more disappointed than ever. His mouth was downturned into a frown. His eyes were downcast. "It ain't no use, Pinto and Nip," he said as he handed Nip a few scraps of meat and fed me a scoop of oats. "No one wants to hear our story, let alone share it. I even met with the great Jack London. He's a famous author. I was sure he would want to write a book about us." George dropped his chin and shook his head. "He just said it was my story, not his." He stretched his thin body down on the hay, his arms folded under his head. Nip curled up beside him.

George gazed up at the dust-and-cobweb-covered rafters as he absentmindedly scratched Nip behind the ears. "Guess it'll be up to me to write the story," he said in a whisper. He jerked up into a sitting position. "Let's go home."

The next day, Nip and I were led up a steep, wooden ramp onto an enormous ship tied to a dock. I was reminded of the ferry we took from Bainbridge Island more than three years earlier. However, this ship was much, much bigger and it had a smokestack sticking up from the top, belching gray clouds of smoke. I followed George as he led me down a narrow passageway between wooden crates. I soon found myself in a small, dark, wooden, box-like room on the deck of the ship. Nip was with me. The room shook and rocked, and for the next week I struggled to remain standing. I got very little sleep, being terribly nervous and confused. I had no idea what was happening.

George came by to see us during the daylight hours. He brought us food and water and spoke soothingly to us. "You boys doin' okay?" he asked. But when the tiny window in the door became dark, signifying the arrival of the night, we were left alone.

"What are we doing here, Nip?" I asked.

"George said we were going home, but I've never seen a home like this," the dog said.

"Nor have I," I answered as the ship tipped, nearly knocking me over. "I hope you're right and that we will end up somewhere that doesn't shake and rock."

"At least George is still with us," Nip pointed out. "We can trust him to take care of us."

We docked in Seattle on a rainy, windy day. I stumbled off the ship, having trouble walking after standing for so long. My legs nearly buckled under me as soon as I stepped on the stationary shore, so accustomed was I to the rocking motion of the steamer.

No one was there to greet us and welcome us home. Even the people scurrying around the dock were too busy to pay us any mind.

"Well, it's just the three of us," George said as he rubbed my neck then bent down and scratched Nip behind the ears. "It's just the three of us, now."

CHAPTER 37

Back at Home

At long last, I was back in my home…the place I was born. It felt good. Nip, George and I settled into a tiny cabin close to town but far enough out to have room for a little barn and paddock for me.

Every day, George brushed me off, saddled me up, and took me for a hack along the tree-lined dirt roads that covered the island. Nip trotted along beside us.

George greeted people as we passed, stopping frequently so friends and neighbors could give me a treat. I especially loved the apples that are so plentiful around here.

It took me quite a while to gain back the weight I had lost on our long journey but, eventually, I was as plump and shiny as one of those polished apples.

When George was not riding, he spent his days in the cabin. I could hear a clickity clack, clickity clack, clickity clack, Bing. Clickity clack, clickity clack, clickity clack, Bing. Silence was always followed by a ripping sound and George shouting. "I write it sweet enough, but it always comes out sour."

I learned that George was trying to write a book about our journey, but it wasn't coming out very well.

After a couple of years back home, I noticed that Nip was moving more slowly when we went for our hack in the forest. Some days he didn't come with us at all, preferring to sleep on the sagging, wooden porch attached to the front of the house. I noticed that he was getting gray hairs over his muzzle and his eyes seemed to have lost their sparkle and appeared cloudy. One day, Nip didn't get up to greet us when we returned from our daily ride through the forest. My heart sank. I knew I was losing my friend. I watched as George carried Nip into the cabin. I never saw Nip again.

PINTO!

George started staying out late at night and coming home smelling of alcohol. I knew the smell from the times Slim drank too much and caused all sorts of trouble on the trail. Some days, after these late nights, George wouldn't come out to the barn to feed me until the sun was well up in the sky.

Life changed for me on a cold, windy, rainy day. I remember the day well. George came out to feed me just before the gray clouds turned black. He tossed some hay to me before rushing away. In his hurry, he forgot to latch the gate to my paddock. I glanced over and noticed it was open but continued to eat my dinner.

Sometime during the night, the rain and wind stopped. I ventured out of my stall and walked up to the open gate. George's little cabin was still dark, so I knew he had not returned even though it was quite late. I used my muzzle to push open the gate far enough for me to get my body through. My eyes were still moderately good in the darkness and I knew the way into town from my frequent trips with George. I decided to go check on him.

George could no longer afford to have shoes put on my hooves. As a result, I slipped on the muddy surface of the narrow drive leading out from our cabin. I fell to my knees and got my front legs quite dirty. *No matter*, I told myself. *I need to find George and bring him home.*

I walked slowly and carefully to the end of our lane to where a road passed by our property. I knew if I turned to the left, I would get to town. The footing on the road was better, as there were drainage ditches along both sides of the road to gather and carry away the water. I picked up a trot.

I had nearly reached town when I noticed an odd-shaped object lying in one of the ditches. In the darkness, it was hard to tell what it was, so I decided to investigate. I slowed to a walk and stepped up to the edge of the ditch. My ears pricked forward as I lowered my muzzle and snorted. I realized that it was a person and, by the familiar smell mixed with the odor of alcohol, I recognized immediately who it was. Even though his face was in the water, I knew it was George.

I stretched my neck down and used my lips to nuzzle the back of his head. He didn't respond. I clamped my teeth around the collar of his jacket and pulled. My hooves began to slip on the edge of the ditch, but I struggled harder. Slowly, I was able to drag him out of the ditch and onto the road.

I knocked and pushed him with my nose. After several tries, I was able to turn him over. I put my nostrils next to his mouth and blew out warm air. Nothing. I nudged him again and blew warm air into his nose and mouth. Still no response.

My heart sank. I knew there was nothing more I could do. I folded my front legs and lowered myself to the ground beside George and waited there until the daylight made its sad appearance.

CHAPTER 38

The Island Pet

The gloomy day I lost George, I became my own horse. From that day on, no one was my master. The little island of Bainbridge became my home, its occupants became my friends.

Each day I visited the local feed store for a scoop of grain. If no one was available to give me some, I just latched my teeth onto a burlap bag, shook my head, and ripped the sack open. I nibbled on the oats until someone came out the door of the building and shooed me away.

"Off you go, Pinto," said the man who owned the feed store. "That's enough for you, today."

I trotted away, knowing I'd be back.

The island was home to several children, all of whom considered me their personal pet. I patiently allowed them to crawl beneath my belly, braid flowers into my tail and shaggy mane, and even ride on my back without a saddle, sometimes two or three at a time.

I was everyone's favorite guest at birthday parties. I remember one little girl who tied colorful ribbons all over my body and fed me cake. "Thanks for coming to my party," she said, as she stroked my white blaze.

On cold, rainy days, I found shelter in an old, abandoned barn on the north end of the island. Once the rain stopped, I ventured out to fill my stomach with the long grasses that grew between the giant fir trees.

It was a good life for a horse.

As I grew older and my eyesight grew dimmer, I began to worry that my great adventure with the Overland Westerners would be forgotten. George was gone. Nip was gone. I hadn't seen Slim, Jay or Fat for many summers.

So, I leave it to you to remember us. And when you think of us, remember that we had a dream, though at times I will admit it was more like a nightmare. But with all we went through, we reached our goal. We made it to every state capital and ended our journey at the San Francisco

World's Fair, just as George had planned. And that was quite a feat.

Perhaps no one else cared, but we did. We lived it; we suffered through it; and we got to the end. We didn't become rich and famous as George expected, but we knew in our hearts that we had done what we set out to do, and there is a treasure to be had in knowing that.

The Story Behind the Story of Pinto

*George Beck on Pinto. Photo Courtesy of the
Bainbridge Island Historical Museum*

The Panama Canal—one of mankind's greatest
engineering feats—was approaching completion.
After thirty arduous, deadly years, the United
States would finish, on August 15, 1914, what the
French had begun in 1881: a shortcut from the
Atlantic to the Pacific, across what had been part
of Colombia until a U.S.-backed revolution
created a new nation.

Plans were underway for a world's fair to celebrate the Canal's completion. The Panama-Pacific International Exposition would open in San Francisco on February 20, 1915 and run until almost Christmas. The Liberty Bell was being transported cross-country by railroad to be on display; the world's first steam locomotive would be there, too, among many marvels of the new century. There would even be a telephone line from New York to the West Coast.

To George Beck, a logger on Bainbridge Island, Washington, the coming extravaganza represented a unique opportunity. "We're born to the saddle. We have the nags and gear. Let's ride to every state Capital in the Union. Let's get ourselves a reputation. Let's make the longest horseback ride on record!" George W. Beck

As a horse-lover since birth, who never recovered from the disease, I thought I had read everything that involved a horse. Then I stumbled across George Beck's quote while researching an article for my blog about noble and great horses.

The longest horseback ride on record? I've never even heard of it, I thought, which is saying something for me.

I was curious. I began searching on the Internet for anything I could find about the Overland

PINTO!

Westerners and Pinto, the only horse to make it through the whole, long, arduous journey. I found that the Cowboy Museum in Oklahoma City had the rights to many of the old photographs I came across. So, while staying in Oklahoma for a book signing at the National Little Britches Championship Rodeo, I took a side trip to the museum. The research librarian wasn't even aware that they had the collection—that's how much dust it had gathered. But, with enough searching she was able to find a forgotten old box in the basement labeled "Overland Westerners." I lifted the lid and discovered my first pot of gold.

My husband and I spent several hours making photocopies of articles and pictures. My file labeled "Pinto" began to fill up.

With more searching, I discovered that the Bainbridge Island Historical Museum in Port Blakely, Bainbridge Island, Washington also had a collection of materials. I called them and spoke with Tim Bird, the museum's volunteer coordinator. The enthusiasm in his voice was palpable as he told me about their collection of pictures and diaries, and their permanent exhibit about the Overland Westerners. I arranged to travel to the island and, when I arrived, was greeted with my own worktable, computer, and stacks of material…an author's dream.

I immersed myself in the journals written by George Beck and Raymond "Fat" Rayne. I suffered with them through the blizzards, thunderstorms and scorching heat. I cringed when rats crawled over their prone bodies as they tried to sleep in deserted barns. I ached as door after door was slammed in their faces.

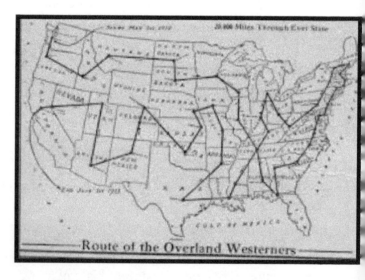

Map of the route taken by the Overland Westerners courtesy of the Bainbridge Island Historical Museum.

I realized that, had I been on this journey, my enthusiasm would surely have ebbed and flowed.

Yet, I marveled that George was always at high tide. I wondered if the draw of fame and fortune was so strong, so blinding, that he could see past all the struggles. Or was there, perhaps, something more that kept him going? Was he tired of living

Photograph of the Calendar the Overland Westerners sold to raise money courtesy of the Bainbridge Island Historical Museum.

on a tiny island and infected with a wanderlust so all-encompassing that there was no room for discouragement?

The more reading I did, the more my heart, a horse-lover's heart, went out to Pinto. I couldn't stop thinking about what he experienced. As the men suffered, surely Pinto and the other horses did, too. Yet Pinto and George clearly shared a common trait that bonded them together—a determination to see it to the end, to never give up. That sweet, little horse had a heart as big as the entire country and I loved him for it.

When it came time to write this book, my thoughts drifted to one of my favorite childhood stories, "Black Beauty." *That's how this story needs to be told,* I thought. *Pinto needs to tell this story himself.*

The Capitals Visited by the Overland Westerners

The Overland Westerners with Governor Clark in front of the Iowa State Capitol. Photo Courtesy of The Bainbridge Island Historical Museum.

The Capitals:

Order and dates taken from their journals and photographs.

Olympia Washington   May 1, 1912

Salem, Oregon   May 11, 1912

Boise, Idaho   June 18, 1912

Helena, Montana   July 21, 1912

Bismarck, North Dakota	September 12, 1912
Pierre, South Dakota	September 26, 1912
St. Paul, Minnesota	October 27, 1912
Madison, Wisconsin	November 25, 1912
Springfield, Illinois	December 13, 1912
Nashville, Tennessee	January 17, 1913
Montgomery, Alabama	April 22, 1913
Tallahassee, Florida	May 15, 1913
Atlanta, Georgia	June 5, 1913
Columbia, South Carolina	June 24, 1913
Raleigh, North Carolina	July 7, 1913
Richmond, Virginia	July 28, 1913
Washington D.C.	August 1913
Annapolis, Maryland	August 18, 1913
Dover, Delaware	Summer 1913
Trenton, New Jersey	August 28, 1913
Hartford, Connecticut	September 10, 1913
Providence, Rhode Island	September 14, 1913
Boston, Massachusetts	September 20, 1913
Concord, New Hampshire	September 26, 1913
Augusta, Maine	August 18, 1913
Montpelier, Vermont	October 1913
Albany, New York	November 12, 1913
Harrisburg, Pennsylvania	December, 1913
Charleston, West Virginia	December 29, 1913
Cincinnati, Ohio	Winter 1914
Lansing, Michigan	February 24, 1914

PINTO!

Indianapolis, Indiana	Spring 1914
Frankfort, Kentucky	March 16, 1914
Jackson, Mississippi	April 27, 1914
Baton Rouge, Louisiana	May 8, 1914
Austin, Texas	June 18, 1914
Little Rock, Arkansas	Summer 1914
Jefferson City, Missouri	Summer 1914
Des Moines, Iowa	September 18, 1914
Lincoln, Nebraska	Fall 1914
Topeka, Kansas	October 15, 1914
Oklahoma City, Oklahoma	November 13, 1914
Cheyenne, Wyoming	December 23, 1914
Denver, Colorado	December 29, 1914
Albuquerque, New Mexico	January 25, 1915
Phoenix, Arizona	March 3, 1915
Salt Lake City, Utah	Spring 1915
Carson City, Nevada	Spring 1915
Sacramento, California	May 24, 1915

Arrived at the Panama-Pacific International Exposition in San Francisco on June 1, 1915— Right on Schedule!

Sources and Acknowledgements

There are three places in the United States that have materials on the Overland Westerners and their incredible journey. The first one I visited is the National Cowboy Museum in Oklahoma City, OK. Their Donald C. Dickinson Research Center has an incredible collection of original photographs of the Overland Westerners depicting nearly every stop in front of a capitol building as well as some other interesting photos.

The Bainbridge Island Historical Museum in Port Blakely, Bainbridge Island, Washington has a fabulous, permanent exhibit of their hometown heroes as well as several of the original journals written by George Beck and Raymond Rayne. They also have an extensive collection of newspaper and magazine articles that were written about them. Their Volunteer Coordinator, Tim Bird, and their museum Curator, Rick Chandler, were an enthusiastic and invaluable help on this project. Without them, this book could not have been written.

Photo of the author with a driftwood statue of Pinto in front of the Bainbridge Island Historical Museum

There is also a collection of materials in the Mason County Historical Society Museum in Shelton, Washington.

A special thank you to author Denny Dressman who believed in this book and kept me going.

Bibliography

Most of my information was taken from the journals written by George Beck and Raymond Rayne in the possession of the Bainbridge Island Historical Museum. Some details were created from my imagination. For example, I found no explanation for how any of the horses died along the trail, so I created the story where Dolly died of colic and Molly died of a rattlesnake bite. I also created the dialogue based upon the writings in the journals.

Articles:

1. Hartstone, Judith. "Three-Year Journey No Mere Tall Tale From the Saddle." *West Sound*, Sunday, April 17, 1994
2. O'Reilly, CuChullaine. "Four Forgotten Heroes Rode 20,000 Miles." *Riding Holidays*, July 23, 2002 (Also published in *The Long Riders' Guild* journal)
3. Osier, C.A. "Joe." "20,000 Miles in the Saddle." *Empire Magazine of the Denver*

Post, August 23rd and 30th, 1964, pages 10-14

4. Osier, C.A. "Joe." "Saddled, Bridled, Ready to Ride." *Frontier Times*, December-January 1967 pages 36-39 (Also published in *The Paint Horse Journal*, date unknown)

5. Osier, C.A. "Joe." "U.S. Horseback Tour of 1912." The Seattle Times, Sunday, July 18, 1948

6. "Overland Westerners to Ride into Mankato on the Morrow; Unique Party on Long Journey." *Daily Free Press* (Mankato, Minnesota) Friday, October 18, 1912

7. "Overland Westerners to Visit Fair City." *The Daily Huronite*, (South Dakota) Wednesday, October 2, 1912.

Songs:

1. "The Trail of the Lonesome Pine," 1913, with lyrics by Ballad MacDonald and music by Harry Carroll. Believed to be first recorded in New York on 28 March 1913 by the Spanish-American tenor Manuel Romain and released in June of that year on issue number 1743 of the Edison Blue Amberol label.

2. "There is a Boarding House," Published in *Two Hundred Old-time Songs* [Mark Twain's annotated songbook (New York: J. S. Ogilvie, 1896)]

ABOUT THE AUTHOR

Award-winning author, M.J. Evans grew up in Lake Oswego, Oregon, and graduated from Oregon State University. She spent five years teaching junior high and high school students before retiring to raise her five children. She is a life-long equestrian and enjoys competing in Dressage and riding in the beautiful Colorado Mountains.

Connect with her on her website:
www.dancinghorsepress.com
Facebook pages: Margi Evans, Behind the Mist, In the Heart of a Mustang or North Mystic.
Instagram: mjevansbooks

TEACHERS and HOME SCHOOLERS -Visit the website for instructions on how you can receive a FREE study guide. www.dancinghorsepress.com

Additional Titles by M.J. Evans

The Mist Trilogy-Behind the Mist,
Mists of Darkness, The Rising Mist

Gold medal from the Mom's Choice Award

First Place - Equus Film Festival

North Mystic

First Place in the Purple Dragonfly Awards

In the Heart of a Mustang

First Place - Literary Classics Awards

First Place – Equus Film Festival

Second Place – Nautilus Awards

Second Place – Readers' Favorite Awards

The Centaur Chronicles-
The Stone of Mercy, The Stone of Courage,
The Stone of Integrity, The Stone of Wisdom

Gold, Silver and Bronze Medals – Feathered Quill

Silver Medal – Readers' Favorite Awards

PINTO!

Finalist – Book Excellence Award

First Place – Equus Film Festival

Purple Dragonfly Award

New Apple ebook award

PERCY –
The Racehorse Who Didn't Like to Run

First Place – Purple Dragonfly Award

Silver Medal – Feathered Quill Awards

Equestrian Trail Guidebooks:

Riding Colorado-

Day Trips from Denver With Your Horse

Riding Colorado II-

Day Trips from Denver With Your Horse

Riding Colorado III-

Day and Overnight Trips With Your Horse

All fiction titles are available on the Website:

www.dancinghorsepress.com and wherever books are sold.

CPSIA information can be obtained
at www.ICGtesting.com
Printed in the USA
LVHW012118081219
639847LV00001B/61/P